Absorbing
the Essence

Simon Blow

First published 2010
Copyright © 2010 Simon Blow

National Library of Australia
Cataloguing-in-Publication data:

Simon Blow

Absorbing the Essence

ISBN: 978-0-9750480-8-5

Published by:
The Genuine Wisdom Centre
PO Box 446
Summer Hill NSW 2130
Australia
(www.genuinewisdomcentre.com)

Editing:
Essence Writing (www.essencewriting.com.au)

Cover design and layout:
Determind Design (www.determind.com.au)

Diagrams:
Avril Carruthers and John Bennetts

Disclaimer
The intention of this book is to present information and practices that have been used throughout China for many years. The information offered is according to the author's best knowledge and is to be used by the reader at his or her own discretion and liability. Readers should obtain professional advice where appropriate regarding their health and health practices. The author disclaims all responsibility and liability to any person, arising directly or indirectly from taking or not taking action based upon the information in this publication.

This book is dedicated to

... all those seeking harmony in their life

Contents

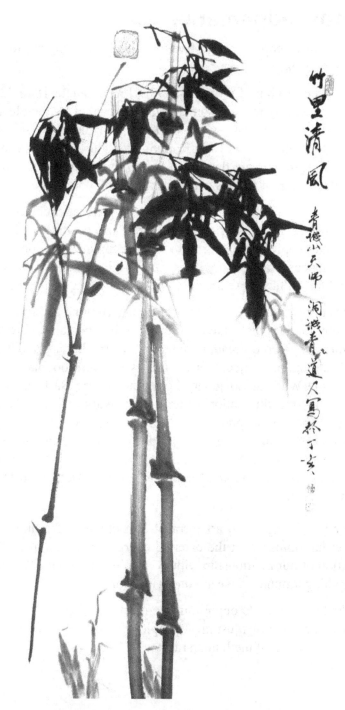

Black Bamboo by Taoist Priest Grand Master Tang, Qing Cheng Shan
Green City Mountain, Sichuan Province, China. October 2007

Acknowledgements

There are many people I would like to thank for helping me to compile and develop this book.

Since I started teaching full-time in 1992, I have taught 18 to 22 classes per week – the best way to learn something is to teach it, as the old saying goes. This is especially relevant when working with the universal life force Qi energy, as it is important to be in front of people to share this energy. Qigong Master Jack Lim told me that when you are teaching a class, think of it as being with a group of friends and sharing. Thank you for this advice, Jack.

I would like to thank all those friends who have attended my classes and workshops over the years. I get many ideas and positive feedback from the students and people I meet and from those who have generously shared their own experiences. I'm not sure if we have original ideas or if, when the heart opens and the Qi flows, we are simply all one. Again, thank you.

My great appreciation to Grand Master Zhong Yunlong for sharing the Qigong cultivation practices that I have presented in this book. I would like to thank Lynn Guilhaus for proofreading, editing, researching and additional writing and for bringing this project to life. Thank you John Kooyman for the original photos of the Wudang Longevity Form and Sitting Ba Duan Jin, and Avril Carruthers for the illustrations; they are all works of art. Thank you John Bennetts for the original photos and drawing adaptations for the Qigong warm-up, and Master Zhang Cheng Cheng and Master Liu Changlin for the Chinese writing. Thank you to Adriene Hurst for additional editing, Ivan Finnegan for original cover design, and Mamun Khan from Determind Design for the layout and design.

We refer to Qigong as an art form. It is a process of refining our internal energy to harmonise with the external energy or environment. It's our own observation of our relationship with everything around us. We are influenced by everything around us, we are one with everything.

I have had the fortunate opportunity to meet many great masters, professors and doctors, but mainly, just great people who are committed to contributing to the development of the human race.
Thank you.

About the Author: Simon Blow

A near-fatal accident at the age of nineteen lead Simon to investigate various methods of healing and rejuvenation, a path he has been following ever since. Simon is a Sydney-based (Australia) master teacher (Laoshi) of the ancient Chinese art of longevity and has been leading regular classes for beginning and continuing students since 1990.

Having travelled the world to learn and explore this ancient art, Simon has received extensive training and certification from many respected sources: Traditional Chinese Medical Hospitals and Daoist Monasteries in China, Buddhist Monasteries in Australia, and Hindu Ashrams in India. He has been given authority to share these techniques through his teachings and publications.

Simon received World Health Organisation Certification in Medical Qigong clinical practice from the Xiyuan Hospital in Beijing and is a Standing Council Member of the World Academic Society of Medical Qigong in Beijing. He has also been initiated into Dragon Gate Daoism and given the name of Xin Si, meaning Genuine Wisdom.

His dedication, compassion and wisdom also make Simon a sought-after keynote speaker and workshop facilitator. By demand he has created a series of Book/DVD sets and guided meditation CDs. He also helps produce CDs for the Sunnatram Forest Monastery, the YWCA Encore program and a series of Meditation CDs for children and teenagers.

China holds a special place in Simon's heart. He has had the great fortune to travel to China on many occasions to study Qigong, attend international conferences, tour the sacred mountains and experience the rich culture of the Chinese people. Since 1999 he has been leading unique study tours to China so he could take people to the source and give them the opportunity to experience first-hand this ancient healing practice.

Romanisation of Chinese words

The Genuine Wisdom Centre uses the Pinyin romanisation system of Chinese to English. Pinyin is a name for the system used to transliterate Chinese words into the Roman alphabet. The use of Pinyin was first adopted in the 1950s by the Chinese government, and it became official in 1979 when it was endorsed by the People's Republic of China.

Pinyin is now standard in the People's Republic of China and in several world organisations, including the United Nations. Pinyin replaces the Wade-Giles and Yale systems.

Some common conversions:

Pinyin	Also spelled as	Pronunciation
Qi	Chi	Chee
Qigong	Chi Kung	Chee Kung
Taiji	Tai Chi	Tai Jee
Taijiquan	Tai Chi Chuan	Tai Jee Chuen
Gongfu	Kung Fu	Gong Foo
Dao	Tao	Dao
Daoism	Taoism	Daoism
Dao De Jing	Tao Teh Ching	Dao Te Ching

How to use this book

Traditionally we follow the teacher/master and this balances our energy. The book gives detailed instructions on how to perform the movements and provides additional theory and history to complement the practises.
To view videos showing the shape of the movements please visit our YouTube channel
www.yoututbe.com/simonblowqigong

It's important to learn from an experienced qualified teacher and to practise regularly to master the movements yourself. Attending regular classes provides consistent practice and refinement and the energy of the group nurtures and supports everyone. It's important not to stray too far from the flock.

Chapter 1
Introduction

Absorbing the Essence

Introduction

The concept of Qi energy has been an integral component of Eastern philosophy and medicine for thousands of years. However, there is no single accepted definition of Qi. Some people think that Qi is an electric energy, while others believe it is magnetic energy, or heat energy. Scientists have long been interested in measuring Qi but it cannot yet be measured by any medical science or explained via physics. However, there is a lot of science behind Qigong – more so than any other form of Energy Medicine.

Qi is central to Daoist philosophy – it is the natural force which fills the universe, the universal spirit, the energy behind the continuous movement of molecules and atoms. In Japan it is called 'ki', and in India, 'prana' or 'shakti'. The ancient Egyptians referred to it as 'ka', and the ancient Greeks as 'pneuma'. Native Americans call it 'Great Spirit' and for Christians, it is the 'Holy Spirit'. In Hawaii it is known as 'ha' or 'mana'.

The Chinese believe in Three Powers of the universe: Heaven (Tian), Earth (Di) and Human (Ren). Heaven Qi is the most important, consisting of forces such as sunshine, moonlight, gravity and energy from the stars and planets. Earth Qi is controlled by Heaven Qi and according to Chinese theory it is made up of lines and patterns of energy, the earth's magnetic field and underground heat. Each individual person has their own Qi field which always seeks balance. All natural things, including humans, plants and animals, grow within and are influenced by the natural cycles of Heaven Qi and Earth Qi.

According to Chinese Medicine, within the human body there are two major types of Qi: Congenital Qi (Prenatal or Ancestral Qi) which is the Qi that we are born with; and Acquired Qi (post-natal) which is the Qi that we generate within our lifetime from the air that we breathe, the food that we eat, Qigong practice and being in harmony with the universe. The Qi that flows at the surface of the body, as a protective sheathe, is called Wei Qi or protective Qi.

Each internal organ also has its own Qi. According to Daoist cosmology, the two most fundamental forms of Qi are Yin Qi and Yang Qi – the primordial feminine and masculine energies. As well as Heaven Qi and Earth Qi, many Qigong practices utilise the Qi that emanates from trees, flowers, lakes and mountains. If our eating and breathing patterns are healthy, and our Qigong practice strong, we can generate a surplus of Acquired Qi, which can then be used to supplement our Congenital Qi. This can aid in many inherited conditions.

We depend on nature for our development and growth - everything in the world comes from the interaction of Heaven Qi (Yang) and Earth Qi (Yin). We breathe to absorb Heaven Qi and eat to absorb Earth Qi. The essence of the food we consume is transported by the Spleen to the Lung to combine with fresh air to produce Zong Qi. Supported by Original Qi stored in the kidneys, Zong Qi is then transformed into True Qi which in its Yin aspect becomes Ying Qi (which flows through the meridians) and in its Yang aspect becomes Wei Qi (which protects us from external pathogens).

In Daoism, Qi has four major actions: ascending, descending, entering and exiting. When Qi is flowing smoothly, and there is balance between its ascending/descending and entering/exiting functions, then we are healthy. Inner Alchemy reveals the human body to be the meeting-place of Heaven and Earth. During Qigong practice we draw Heaven Qi down from above and Earth Qi up from below. Even when we're not doing Qigong practices, we absorb Heaven Qi with every breath we take, and Earth Qi through the food we eat.

This is why there are not specific Qigong exercises for different conditions as Qigong helps balance and harmonise the Qi. When the Qi is in order the mind, body and spirit will also be in order.

Neijing Tu

The Neijing Tu, which translates to the 'Inner Landscape' or the 'Inner Circulation of the Human Body', is an ancient map or chart of inner vision used in the Daoist tradition.

Legend explains that the Neijing Tu was originally carved on a rock, high up in the mountains at a secret cultivation location. It was later carved onto a wooden tablet and rubbings were made onto paper. I received this copy which has been photographed from the White Cloud Monastery in Beijing.

The book Huangdi Neijing (The Yellow Emperor's Internal Canon of Chinese Medicine), which in 2,500 BC described the basic theory of Traditional Chinese Medicine and is still used today, refers to the Neijing Tu. Lao Tzu, author of the Dao De Jing, also makes reference to the Neijing Tu.

The Dao adept saw the human body as a microcosm of the natural world. Its anatomy was a landscape with mountains, rivers, streams, a lake, pool, forest, fire, and stars – a natural harmonious landscape.

The right-hand border of the diagram represents the spinal column and skull and is outlined by a stream that represents the spinal cord; this stream represents the Governing Channel or Du Channel and allows Yin and Yang energy to flow through the body. The head is dominated by a chain of mountains representing Yang energy and corresponds to the celestial realm.

The lower part of the torso is dominated by the Yin image of water. This water is made to flow upward toward the head by a girl and boy on treadmills (Yin and Yang). The water turns into fire as it rises up the spinal column, representing its transformation into Yang energy. The remaining images in the central torso also represent the flow of Yin and Yang energies and the alchemical changes occurring within the fields or Dan Tians.

The Qigong cultivation practices presented in this book –'Absorbing the Essence' – help stimulate the Heavenly Orbit which allows the internal landscape to become healthy and to harmonise with the external landscape or environment. Ultimately we can allow our energies to merge with the universe.

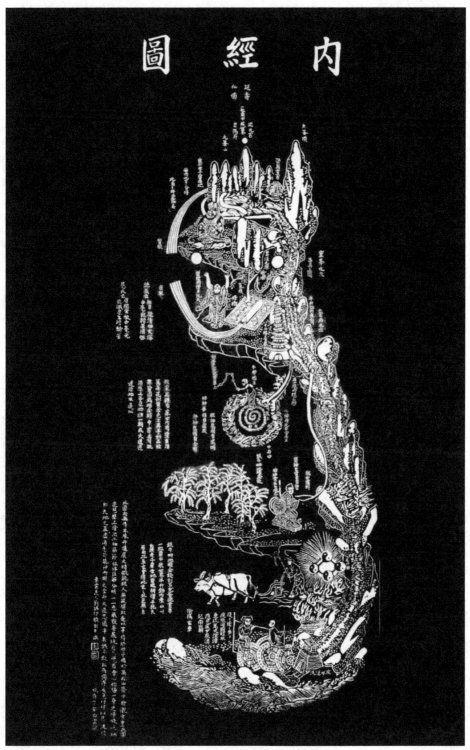

Neijing Tu

Chapter 2
Absorbing the Essence

Absorbing the Essence

Absorbing the Essence

This Book/DVD set is a compilation of the teachings I received on my first two trips to Wudangshan (Shan translates to 'mountain') in China. The Wudang Mountains stretch 400km across Hubei province and Wudangshan is revered as one of the sacred Daoist mountains in China.

While leading my first study group to China in September 1999, we visited Wudang Mountain and met Grand Master Zhong Yunlong. Master Zhong – an engaging, energetic man – was one of the main Daoist Priests from the Purple Cloud Temple, a large monastery with about 100 monks and nuns nestled high up in the mountains. We had a formal meeting with him during which we drank green tea grown on the mountain and discussed Daoist ideas and our reasons for being there.

Master Zhong ran a small school with about 12 full-time students learning the Daoist arts which included martial arts (Wushu), Tai Chi, Qigong and meditation. He would also take small groups of foreign students, like my group, to help subsidise the running of the school. Master Zhong gave us a demonstration of a Tai Chi form and then asked me to give a demonstration as well. Afterwards he made some comments, commending me on the years of practice that I had done, and gave a detailed talk about the importance of the breath and breathing.

The next morning we commenced our training in the Taiji Hunyuan Zhuang Qigong, which translates to 'the interaction of Yin and Yang', 'absorbing the primordial essence of the universe', and 'energy work'. We shortened the name to the Wudang Longevity form. It's a very simple form, but expresses a very strong energy, especially when we were practising it with Master Zhong at Mt Wudang. As we left, I promised Master Zhong that I would return in 12 months with another group of students, whom I would train in the Longevity form, and we would be ready to learn more. He gave me a knowing look and nodded.

To my word, I returned to China with my second study group in September

2000. When we visited Wudangshan, Master Zhong welcomed us like old friends. I lead the group, which included students and other Tai Chi/Qigong teachers in the Longevity form, in a demonstration in front of Master Zhong, other Daoist Priests and the students of his school. He complimented us on our practice and dedication. We spent quality time with Master Zhong in his private rooms, discussing the Daoist understanding of energy cultivation and spirituality. We all shared stories of our experiences which contributed to a very special occasion for all who were there.

He asked us what we would like to learn next. I personally don't have much interest in the martial arts and focus mainly on meditation and spiritual understanding, so he suggested teaching us a Daoist Meditation practice with a history of 2,000 years. The next morning we started our instruction in the Sitting Ba Duan Jin, or 'Life Nurturing Qigong'.

Master Zhong 1999   With Master Zhong 2000

When we had completed our training, I asked Master Zhong if he could give me some type of certification for the two Daoist Qigong styles that he had taught me. Although his school doesn't issue certificates, he agreed to write me a personal letter granting me authority to teach the two cultivation methods that I had learnt at Wudangshan. He said that I had 'absorbed the essence' of these teachings and he gave me the authority to share these techniques to help benefit human wellbeing.

It wasn't until 2004 that my travels took me back to Wudangshan. Master Zhong had been promoted to the head of Mt Wudang and was busy

授 权 书

有澳大利亚.西蒙.贝洛Simon Blow
先生.於一九九年二OOO年西度前来武当山道
教武館.学习太极混元桩功.既.八段锦
養生功.深明其妙.故今特授权於
西蒙.贝洛.Simon Blow先生在澳大利亚
传播专道教武館所学功法造福人类.功
德無量. 值此. 授书.

DOCUMENT GRANTING AUTHORITY

Mr. Simon Blow of Australia has twice travelled (1999 & 2000) to Mt Wudang Shan Taoist Wushu College China to learn Taiji Hunyuan Zhuang Qigong and Badajin Nurturing Life Qigong and through his study has absorbed the essence of these teachings.

武当山道教武館.
館長:
二OOO年

Therefore I specially grant Simon Blow the authority to teach these, spreading the knowledge of these Qigong methods he has learnt at Mt Wudang to contribute to the wellbeing of the human race. May the Meritorious Deeds Be Infinite

Mt. Wudang Shan Taoist Wushu College
Director: Grand Master Zhong   September 24, 2000

travelling with groups of his students promoting Wudang Mountain and the Daoist arts. The Mountain had changed and there were a lot more visitors. When we first visited in 1999 and 2000, it seemed that we were the only ones there.

We practised Qigong and meditation in the grounds of the Purple Cloud Monastery with Master Sui, a Taoist Priest and Master Zhong's second-in-charge. Master Zhong's tiny school had grown and moved to a large hotel complex near the Monastery and was catering for large groups of Chinese and foreign students.

Master Zhong was doing an excellent job of running and promoting the school, and the popular movie Crouching Tiger Hidden Dragon – set at Mt Wudang – had been released and was drawing many people. Wudangshan was becoming a major tourist attraction.

I returned to Wudangshan in 2005 and 2006 with groups of Qigong instructors, hoping to continue my study with Master Zhong, but each time he was away, so on these occasions we practised meditation with Master Yuan, also a Taoist Priest. On my visit in April 2006, I learned that Master Zhong had grown disillusioned with the commercialisation of the area and retreated into the mountain to become a hermit and continue practising the Daoist arts, to merge with the universe, and return to nothingness.

I feel very privileged and honoured to have had the opportunity to spend quality time with Master Zhong. I know that the energy and experiences that I and my companions received and shared with him will always be with us.

The legacy of these teaching is recorded on the DVD 'Qigong - Absorbing the Essence' that I produced in 2003 and now in the book of the same name. As Master Zhong would say, "May the Meritorious Deeds Be Infinite".

The Heavenly Orbit

 Wudangshan is renowned for the development of Tai Chi or Taiji, a Chinese term describing the Yin/Yang symbol. The symbol is a representation of the opposing forces and the wholeness of nature. It is one of the main symbols of Taoism.

The idea of the Taiji symbol cannot be attributed to a single person because we are all influenced by the thinking of previous generations and by our environment. From prehistoric days, our ancestors began to observe the natural cycle of nature; the rising sun following the darkness of night, the continuous change from one season to the next and the changes and adaptations in our environment, including ourselves. As human beings we are a microcosm of our universe and are influenced by our surroundings. This is why Daoist monasteries are typically set in the mountains. There are fewer people and it is easier to harmonise with nature.

The Dao translates to 'the Way'. It's not a religion but a way of harmonising with nature. Its origins are in ancient Chinese culture dating back over 5,000 years. Lao Tzu, a historical figure from 500 BC, was the first great master to write about his understanding of the nature of the Dao. His book, the *Dao De Jing*, is now the basis of most Taoist thought. Some of the other healing arts originating from Daoist tradition include acupuncture, herbal medicine and therapeutic massage.

In governing one's life, there is the subtle path.

This path is ageless. The subtle path has been recognised as Dao, the Integral Way.
Dao is also called the universal subtle energy. At the same time, it is the universal subtle law.

The subtle path can be discerned, yet it is not an ordinary path.

A definition can be given of it; yet it cannot be presented by an ordinary definition with words.

There are no words that can describe it; the subtle path cannot be limited by the definition of words.

The word "indefinable" describes the beginning of the universe.
The word "definable" describes the mother of all, who gives birth to all things and all lives.

Because Dao is subtle energy and at the same time subtle law, it looks like nothing.
It was nothing before the universe was born from it.

This subtle energy gives birth to everything; thus it is the motherly substance of the universe.
It is the mother of all things.

Lao Tzu, Dao De Jing, Chapter One

For the practice of the Daoist Qigong techniques in 'Absorbing the Essence', we refer to the Heavenly Orbit (also known as the Micro Cosmic Orbit) as the flow of energy or Qi in the body. Yang energy rises up the back and Yin energy descends down the front, like a flow of water permeating and stimulating the body's meridian system and balancing its energy system. It enables the blood to flow smoothly, the organs to function correctly, and the body to restore natural harmony. It also helps calm the emotions as the mind is not distracted by imbalances. The Heavenly Orbit resembles a large living Taiji symbol constantly flowing around the body. This energy works on many levels. Every cell of the body is like a tiny moving Taiji. When our Qi or energy is weak, this orbit doesn't flow very smoothly, thus affecting our quality of life.

The ultimate aim of our right of existence is to allow our internal micro environment to harmonise with the external macro environment, and through our work and positive actions, we can help those around us. This enables us to realise ourselves as a living spirit in human form.

LIVING SPIRIT IN PHYSICAL FORM

Other ways of refining our energy

There are many sacred energetic healing places in the world and throughout history people of different faiths and spiritual traditions have travelled and made pilgrimages to these areas. These places have electromagnetic fields; in some locations the fields occur naturally and at others the energy has accumulated over time from worship, meditation and other spiritual practices. The best places have a combination of both. To help develop your own energy I suggest visiting and meditating at some of these amazing places.

I had arranged my first trip to India to align with the end of the second millennium (1999 to 2000) which would also mark 20 years after my accident. I had been back from China only a few months when I joined a small group on a four-week tour of ashrams and Hindu temples around Southern India. I had an urge to go to India mainly to meditate and absorb the essence from the sacred places that I would be visiting.

I was fortunate to spend five days in Tiruvannamalai under the sacred mountain of Arunachala. Arunachala is one of the holiest mountains in India and rises from the plains of Tamil Nadu like a great pyramid. It is very symbolic in the Hindu tradition as it represents the element of Fire and there is a large Hindu Temple for Fire at the base of the mountain. I visited the ashram of Sri Ramana Maharishi and what I experienced here was a complete emptiness of mind, a total state of inner peace. Even though Ramana Maharishi had passed on in 1950 this small ashram is still one of the most powerful spiritual centres in India. He was one of the great Hindu sages of the 20th century and his teachings of 'Who am I?' are a process of self-enquiry that leads to a path of self-realisation. I felt at home and energised here, I returned to the ashram for extended periods of meditation in 2001/2002 and 2009/2010.

Ramanashram, India, 2002

Another sacred healing place is the Sunnataram Forest Monastery. I first met Phra Mana Viriyarampo at the 2001 Sydney Mind Body Spirit Festival where we were both giving presentations on the healing benefits of meditation. Phra Mana is the Abbot of the Sunnataram Forest Monastery, a Theravada Buddhist monastery in the Thai forest tradition. The monastery is situated on the outskirts of Bundanoon, a town in the Southern Highlands, a few hours' drive south of Sydney. Aboriginal people believe that a sacred site is within the monastery area. Since that first meeting we have built a strong friendship and I have been to the Monastery many times to attend retreats led by Phra Mana, conduct my own retreats, and help in whatever way I can. The Gratitude Pagoda has been built by the hard work and dedication of Phra Mana, the Monks of the Monastery, and volunteers. Enshrined within the Pagoda are Buddha relics which are the remains of enlightened beings. Within the Theravada Buddhist tradition when a monk has passed on they are cremated and within the ashes precious stones are sometimes found. These stones are the crystallisation of the spiritual work they have done over their lifetime.

"In the calmness of mind, we will find wisdom and peace. One powerful technique to attain the concentration of mind is to watch the flow of breath. Some people feel it easier to develop their mindfulness with breathing when their bodies are in motion. The exercise of Qi Gong helps many people to relax and, at the same time to gain deeper concentration. Peacefulness of mind arising from this mindful movement will last much longer than sitting meditation. Qi Gong produces physical, mental and spiritual benefits all at once."

Phra Mana Viriyarampo

Is Qigong spiritual?

The understanding of spirituality is different for all of us because there are many things that make us different including our background and culture, even the type of work we do. What I have studied and observed from different traditions is that the basic spiritual understandings are the same. When we help others who are less fortunate than ourselves without any conditions or expectations, we seem to find fulfilment and peace in our life. The practice of Qigong is a way of developing spiritual awareness and when we use this energy to help others it becomes spiritual. I have had the great opportunity to visit the sacred mountains in China and have many meetings with Daoist Priests. When they asked me what I was doing with the Qi that I was developing, I would explain the different groups of people that I work with and they would say I am talking about the high level. The basic level or lower level is the energy cultivation practice; within the Daoist tradition virtue is the highest level. Through our work and effort we are able to become aware of ourselves as a living spirit in physical form and when we use this to aid in the development of the human race we are simply one with the universe.

> *"The wise one helps others without expecting anything in return.*
> *The wise one does not take credit for doing good for other people.*
> *When a person does not think of one's accomplishments, one remains*
> *fresh in life".* **Lao Tzu, Dao De Jing, Chapter Two**

I have great respect for my Daoist teachers and find inspiration from being around them. This tradition is unique as they treat male and female equally. My teacher Grand Master Cheng Zhen, who is in the female form and the Abbott of the Eternal Spring Monastery in Wuhan, would say, "When you are at the highest level there is no difference between the male and female. We are all spirits."

During a retreat at the Sunnatram Forest Monastery in January 2008 I asked the students the question, "Is Qigong spiritual and how is it spiritual for you?" Below are a few of the responses.

> *"Although Qigong began purely as a form of gentle exercise after*
> *a bout of breast cancer, it has become increasingly spiritual as a*
> *practice. Qigong is now a part of my everyday life, in the way I sit,*
> *stand and breathe. As the practice of meditation has become more*
> *natural it has taken on a spiritual dimension. It has begun to affect*
> *the way I think. Qigong has helped me to be more peaceful, less*
> *stressed, more content and more accepting of others."*
> **Tessa Sholl, NSW**

> *"I started Qigong as a purely physical practice and found the*
> *meditation a great idea. Then I visited a Chinese Medicine*
> *Practitioner and discovered where my organ weaknesses were.*
> *The practices and meditations then took on a much deeper and*
> *meaningful aspect. My primary hobby is bird observation and I do a*
> *lot of sitting and slow walking in the bush. I knew there was a lot of*
> *energy around but doing the Qigong practices enables me to bring*

that energy down to become part of me and empower me, and gives me a feeling of oneness with nature. The natural environment was created for a purpose. Through Qigong, that purpose for me is to uplift me spiritually and make my life more peaceful."
Lesley Hook, NSW

"For me Qigong is very spiritual. It provides a space to retreat from the stress-filled, deadline-driven lives so many of us live. It provides a channel to connect with the natural energy surrounding us and I personally have felt the therapeutic benefits (a stiff back that has been plaguing me for a couple of weeks has eased totally after a day and a half of the exercises). The progression into meditation is giving me the space to connect with another level of my persona. This brings me inner peace and contentment and provides a pathway for dealing with situations that are not right in my life." **Bessie Hagen, NSW**

Sunnataram Forest Monastery, 2002

Chapter 3
The Art of Practice

Absorbing the Essence

The Art of Practice*

To get the most out of your practice there are a few basic principles that apply to the styles of Qigong presented in this book.

* This section is repeated from Book 1 – The Art of Life.

Time of day to practise

Generally, you can practise Qigong at any time of the day, so choose a time that best suits you. Remember, we are creatures of habit and you will benefit more if you practise at the same time on each practice day. Some styles of Qigong are best practised at a particular time and sometimes facing a certain direction. In time you will find the best time that suits you.

Exercising in the early morning and late afternoon, when the sun rises and sets, is a very powerful time as it's a natural transition between dark coolness of night (Yin) and the bright warmth of day (Yang). It's important not to look directly into the sun in the early morning or late afternoon as this can cause damage to your eyes. The setting of the sun and transition between Yang and Yin is a time when nature has a great influence on your body. You might notice that birds are very active at this time of the day, as they are in the morning.

I am often asked by new students if it's best to practise with the eyes open or closed, and what does one look at when practising. It may be easier to concentrate when the eyes are closed as we are not distracted by things around us, but the general rule with Qigong is to have the eyes open when moving, looking to the distance but not really looking. Your awareness is on the external (Yang) when the eyes are open and you can absorb the energy or Qi from the environment and universe. It's OK to momentarily close the eyes but it's important to keep them open – not too wide, and relaxed. When practising Qigong meditation or Neigong the eyes are closed as your awareness is now on the internal (Yin).

As a rule, you should not exercise on a full or empty stomach. Instead of eating breakfast, consume liquids as they stimulate stomach-intestine movement which acts as an internal massage. Warm or room temperature water is the best with a slice of lemon. Cold water from the fridge interferes with Qi circulation.

Qigong exercise in the evenings is a way to free your mind and body from the burdens of a busy day and a way of processing the events of the day and letting things go, physically and emotionally. Students often comment on how they get their best night's sleep after attending class. You will then be able to sleep more quietly and recover more fully because the body begins its recovery during Qigong and this continues during sleep.

"When I practise my Qigong in the evening, I sleep much better. Therefore I have more energy the next day." Cherel Waters

We are all a bit different. I wouldn't advise that you practise immediately before going to sleep as it stimulates your energy and may disrupt your sleep. But a few students have told me that when they haven't been able to sleep they get up and practise which calms their mind and body. They then have a restful sleep.

Eating and drinking

For Qigong exercise you need a clear head. Beverages such as alcohol, tea and coffee affect concentration and body functions and if you are not calm and relaxed you will not feel the full benefits of Qigong exercise. It's best to avoid drinking cold fluids during or immediately after practice as this interferes with Qi circulation.

When I was training with Master Ho we began early in the morning at 6.30am and he would take my pulse before and after practice. A few times he became very concerned as my heart rate and organ functions were erratic. He watched me very closely, my movements were slow and smooth and my breath deep and even. After a lot of questions I told him I had a strong espresso coffee half an hour before we started. I have now changed my morning routine and only have warm water or green tea.

Avoid exercising on either an empty stomach or after a full meal. Being distracted by hunger will not help your mental focus so if you are hungry, have something light to eat or something to drink. A full stomach interferes with Qi circulation. The Qi is diverted into the digestive system as stomach juices increase and stomach-intestinal movements occur, leaving very little Qi to circulate elsewhere.

When not to exercise

When we exercise we absorb the good influences from nature and the macrocosm. Similarly, we absorb the influences from turbulent weather conditions. Therefore, it is not good to practise Qigong during bad weather, heavy fog, extreme heat, before or during a thunderstorm, on excessively windy days, or during lunar or solar eclipses. Exercise can begin again when nature is balanced.

Menstruation and pregnancy

Basic Qigong is good to practise during menstruation and pregnancy as it will improve the circulation of Qi, blood and other body fluids.

Women who are menstruating should pay attention to the effects of Qigong exercise. If the exercise produces a negative effect, stop immediately and continue when feeling better.

Special care is also required during pregnancy. Each woman's pregnancy is different, and it is recommended that the expectant mother consult her primary care provider as well as a qualified and experienced Qigong teacher.

"I attended Simon's week-long retreat during my pregnancy and experienced a great release of muscle tension particularly in my arms and shoulders. I also found the meditation that followed the Qigong practice easy to do even though I had never meditated before. It was a very pleasurable experience." Jessica Henley

Where to practise

Qigong can be practised anywhere but some places are better than others. It's best to be undisturbed during Qigong practice to help maintain a concentrated mind. The best places are in nature in the open air where the Heaven (Yang) and Earth (Yin) Qi are most abundant such as in the mountains, beside a waterfall or by the ocean. Near a waterfall or by the ocean is excellent because moving water generates lots of Qi.

If you are practising indoors, try to find a quiet and peaceful space away from draughts, with natural light and fresh air. Avoid excessive noise, TV sets and computers and turn off your mobile phone or set it to silent.

The proximity of some plants should also be avoided. The Oleander plant for example, is known to be poisonous and has a very tense Qi. As you practise you will learn which plants feel relaxing and harmonious. Lovely flowers and large old trees are ideal.

What to wear

There are no rules regarding clothing but since relaxation is important in Qigong try to wear loose comfortable clothing, ideally made of natural fibres such as cotton or silk.

If you are limited in what you can wear, for example if you are at work, loosen your collar and tie, your belt/waistband and remove uncomfortable or high heel shoes. It's important that you wear flat soled shoes or even bare feet are OK. I always wear soft sports shoes as I damaged my feet and ankles a long time ago and I find wearing shoes gives me a bit more support. It's a personal preference. There are many light, soft shoes around today.

Whatever clothing you choose to wear it should not be tight around the waist because the Qi needs to flow easily. Preferably, remove watches and bracelets as they restrict the flow of Qi through the wrist.

If it is chilly, dress appropriately. Feeling cold during a Qigong session can decrease the effectiveness of the exercises particularly if your hands, belly and back are cold. Chilling your kidneys severely restricts your Qi circulation. I often start my practice on colder mornings with gloves, hat and a warm jacket and I can always take them off.

How long to practise

The benefits that are gained from Qigong are proportional to the amount of practice. For beginners, an exercise period of 15 to 30 minutes daily is recommended in order to relax the body and mind and feel the Qi. It is only when the body's carriage is regulated according to Qigong principles that the Qi will flow easily and the benefits of Qigong realised. If you can achieve 30 minutes twice a day, you will notice a marked increase in vitality and peace within a few weeks. If you have major health issues and can manage a couple of hours per day you will soon see a radical improvement in your health and wellbeing. Regardless of your state of health when you begin, any amount of regular practice will improve how you feel.

"I have practised Qigong every day for sixteen years. It helps bring me right into the present moment with a feeling of immense serenity. Each year my health has improved and whenever I experience a set-back, gentle Qigong is always there to help me." Joan Downey

"Over the last few years I have been practising five to six times per week. I am in my 80th year and have gone from wearing a hinged metal knee brace to wearing no brace at all. My knee still creaks but is no longer painful and range of movement is barely restricted." Shirley Chittick

How long does the effect of Qigong exercise last?

Qigong works because the Qi is brought into order and the mind, body and spirit are in harmony. This harmony can be disturbed by arguing, getting excited or annoyed, engaging in strenuous physical activity, eating excessively, and even going to the toilet. If possible, use the toilet beforehand rather than after Qigong exercise because urination and defecation bring the Qi into definite motion.

I often tell my students after a Qigong class that if they have driven a car to get to the class try not to play the radio when they leave because all the senses have been enhanced and body functions are in harmony. In the quietness and stillness you may get good ideas, solve some problems, or if you are with friends you might have some amazing conversations. Look at the beauty of the sky, trees, the divine in all living things. I love to look at clouds. It's a creative time, so use it wisely and the Qi will be with you longer. The more you cultivate your Qi the more in harmony with the universe you will be, improving all aspects of your life.

Chapter 4
Qigong Warm-up

Absorbing the Essence

Qigong warm-up*

*The exercises in this Chapter are the same as the Warm-up exercises in 'The Art of Life'.

Qi is the essence of life

Qi (pronounced Chi) is the foundation of Daoist thinking and Traditional Chinese Medicine (TCM) and is described by Daoist Master Hua-Ching Ni in his book, Tao – the Subtle Universal Law and the Integral Way of Life:

> *"Chi is the vital universal energy that composes, permeates and moves everything that exists. Chi may be defined as the ultimate cause and, at the same time, the ultimate effect of all activity. Chi is the ultimate essence of the universe as well as the law of all movement. When Chi conglomerates, it is called matter. When Chi is diffuse, it is called space. When Chi animates form it is called life. When Chi separates and withdraws, it is called death. When Chi flows, there is health. When Chi is blocked, there is sickness and disease. Chi embraces, circulates through and sustains all things. The planets depend on Chi to regulate their atmosphere, light, weather and the seasons.*

> *"So, it is Chi or vital energy that activates and maintains all life. Chi animates all the processes of the body: the digestion and assimilation of the food we eat, the inhalation and exhalation of air by the lungs, the circulation of the blood, the dissemination of fluids throughout the body and, finally, the excretion of waste products."*

Basic principles

This flow of energy, or Qi, in our body is directly related to our posture and body movements, breath and mental condition. When the mind, body and breath are in harmony, our Qi will also be in harmony. It will flow naturally through the energy channels or meridians of the body, allowing us to connect with the energy of the universe.

When we practise Qigong, it's important not to try too hard. Take your time, allowing the movements and breath to develop. Firstly, we concentrate on the body posture, standing or sitting, keeping the spine upright and letting the muscles and flesh relax around the skeleton. The movements of Qigong help clear the energy blockages in our body. Also known as guiding Qi, your movements will become slow, soft and smooth with regular practice. Then we can concentrate on the breath.

There are a number of different breathing patterns for different styles of Qigong. For the styles presented here we will breathe in and out through the nose to the abdominal area, slowly, deeply and deliberately. When we breathe in, the abdomen gently expands and when breathing out, gently contracts. This is known as natural breathing. In time, the breath will naturally coordinate with the movements, helping the mind focus and allowing a fusion between mind, body and breath.

Qigong warm-up

There are many ways of preparing for Qigong practice. Some parts of the warm-up were taught to me, some I observed by watching people practising in parks in China, and other parts I have developed from my own practice.

The warm-up is not only a way of preparing the mind and body for the Qigong movements that come later, it's also very good exercise. Physically, when we loosen and rotate the joints, we exercise the ligaments and tendons, as well as the membranes which secrete synovial fluid to lubricate the joints. This can benefit many arthritic conditions. Energetically, we clear stagnant energy (Qi) that can accumulate around the joints. According to Traditional Chinese Medicine (TCM), the Qi draws the blood through the body. So when we stimulate the Qi circulation we also stimulate the blood circulation.

It's also very important to focus your awareness, like the light of a torch, on each part of the body as we are exercising it, from head to toe. Through this active meditation we consciously awaken the body by feeling and seeing what we are doing.

Generally, when we have finished the warm-up, we feel warm, tingling and awake.

Basic stance

Stand with feet parallel, shoulder-width apart, as if standing on train tracks. Knees are slightly off lock. Let your weight sink into your legs, feet and into the ground. Keep the coccyx or tail bone slightly tucked in, chest relaxed, and the back straight. Hold your arms away from the body, fingers open and relaxed pointing to the earth, palms facing the body.

With the chin slightly tucked in and the top of the head (Bai Hui point) reaching to the sky as if a silken cord attached to it is lifting the whole body, light the Hui Yin by gently squeezing the pelvic floor. Relax your eyes and face and look out into the distance. Keeping your jaw relaxed, place the tip of your tongue on the top palate of your mouth, just behind the front teeth. Breathe in and out through the nose. When breathing in, let the abdomen push out slightly and as the breath comes out, let the abdomen contract. Just relax, letting the whole body breathe.

With the eyes closed, allow the breath to become smooth and even, and let your mind rest. After a few breaths, concentrate on the out-breath, relaxing from the top of the head to the soles of the feet. Just relax down through the body on the out-breath. After a few more breaths, let the knees and hips sink a bit closer to the ground and feel the pressure go into the feet. Like a tree, follow the roots from the soles of your feet deeply into the ground. As you let the breath out, relax down through the body into the ground, letting the stress and tension of the body dissolve into the earth.

After another few breaths, with your awareness, push up the spine one vertebra at a time, checking that the chin tucks in and letting the head pull away from the body. We seem to stand taller as the top of the head reaches up and touches the sky. Stay in this posture for a few breaths, feeling the peace. With your eyes gradually opening, look out into the distance.

The warm-up movements

Let's start at the top and work down through the body.

Please note that the images are mirrored for the reader; just follow in the same direction.

Shoulder rolls

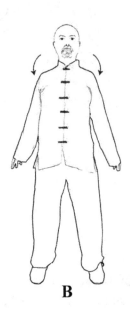

A   B

A   Lift the shoulders and start to rotate them backwards.
B   After about four to six rotations, reverse, gradually increasing your range of movement.

Wrist rotations

A   Slowly raise the arms to shoulder height.

B   Rotate the wrists, as though the fingers are drawing circles in the air. Feel and see the movement of the wrist.

C   After about 4 to 6 rotations stop and come back the other way, gradually increasing your range of movement.

Arm and chest stretch

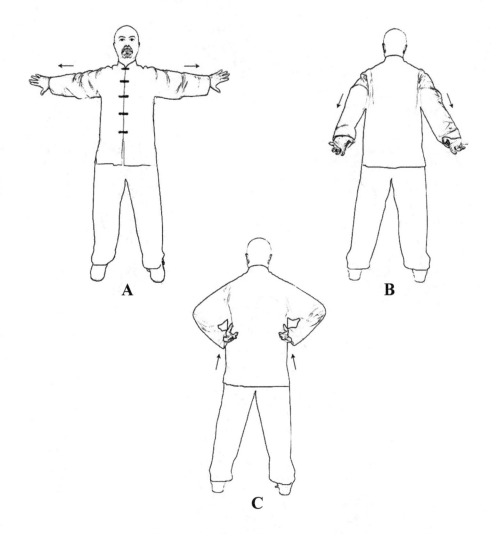

A With your arms still in front of the body, turn your palms out and push to the sides, seeing your chest and rib cage open. Push back and stretch back as far as comfortable.

B Turn your palms up, bend the elbows and bring hands to the front of body brushing by the waist. Repeat 4 times, similar to swimming breaststroke.

C Then repeat 4 times in the opposite direction: with palms up, hands brush by your waist and stretch behind, slowly rotate palms and bring arms in front of body. This movement exercises the chest, shoulders, elbows and wrists.

Body roll

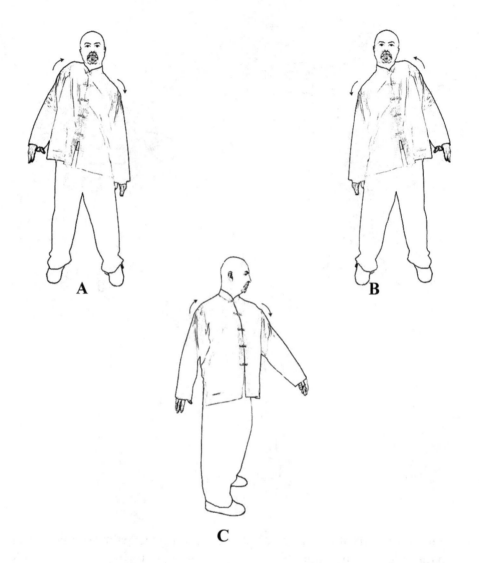

A

B

C

A   Let your arms slowly descend to your sides. Slowly roll one shoulder and then the other, like swimming backwards. With your awareness, feel the motion massage around your shoulders, your chest, around the back of your shoulders and your abdomen, also massaging your back over the kidney area.

B, C After about 8 rotations, stop and come back the other way, and feel the internal massaging.

Hip rotations

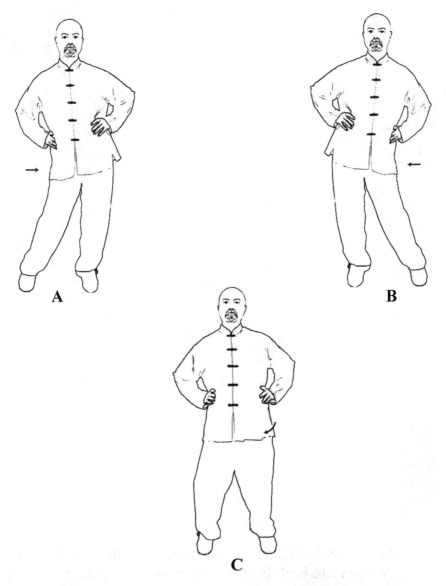

A, B   Place your hands on your waist and start to move your hips from side to side. Relax and feel the movement of the hips.

C   After about three movements to each side, start to move the hips in a circle, gradually increasing your range of movement. Follow the spiralling movement up the spine to the top of your head. Feel and see the movement of the hips. After about 6 rotations, stop and come back the other way.

Walking and massaging the feet

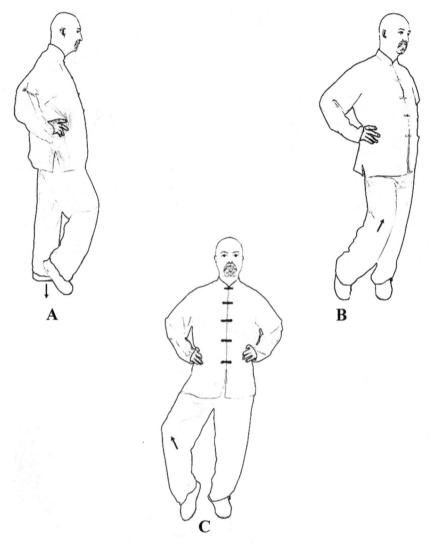

A   Stand with your feet closer together, walking on the spot. Push firmly from the toe to the heel six times to each side, letting the weight of the body massage the feet. Feel and see the tendons, muscles and joints of the feet.

B   Turn and twist while moving your knee across the body, massaging the inside of the foot on the floor towards the big toe. Repeat about 6 times to each side.

C   Stop and push to the outside of the foot, massaging towards the small toe, 6 to each side. Relax, feel and see the movement of the foot.

Foot, leg and hip rotation

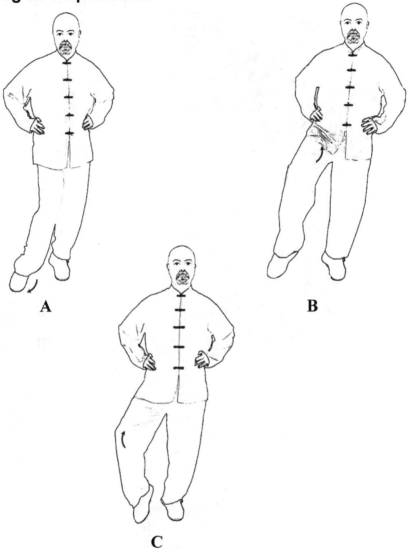

A

B

C

A, B, Standing on your right leg, place the tip of the left big toe on the
C   ground and start to rotate, using your awareness to feel the massage
around your toes and foot. See your ankle rotating and the knee
rotating, right up to your hip. Moving the whole leg together, relax,
feel and see the movement of the leg. Stop and come back the other
way, gradually increasing the range of movement.

Repeat the same process for your right leg and then shake out your legs,
feeling the flow of blood and Qi.

Hand and wrist shaking

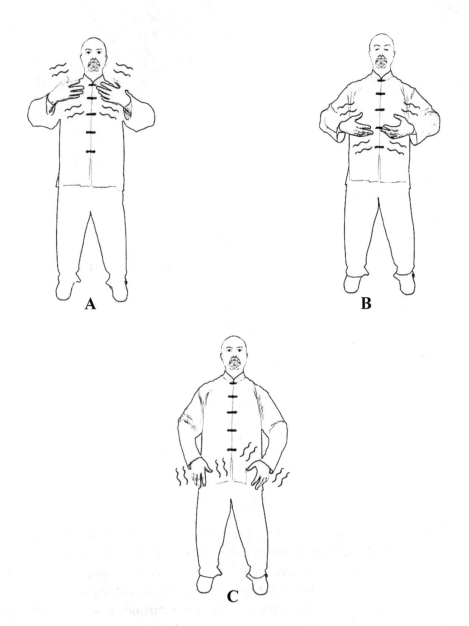

A, B,   Shake your hands, up and down about 6 times, loosening the hands.
C

Hand stretching

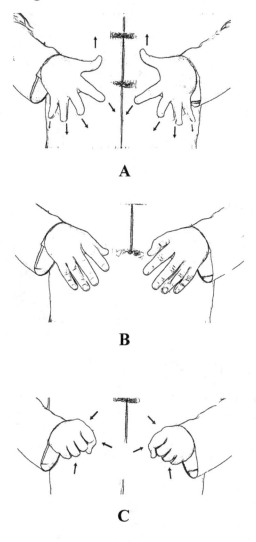

A

B

C

A, B   Extend the hands, stretching all the fingers. It's important not to hold the movement – extend and relax, 6 times.

C   Then clench the fists – again, don't hold. Clench and relax, 6 times.

With the palms up, roll the fingers, starting with the small finger, into a fist and clench with your thumb on outside, 6 times, concentrating on the hands. Stop and roll into a fist the other way, index finger first, 6 times. Again, shake the hands up and down, also moving the knees up and down as you shake the whole body.

Body swings

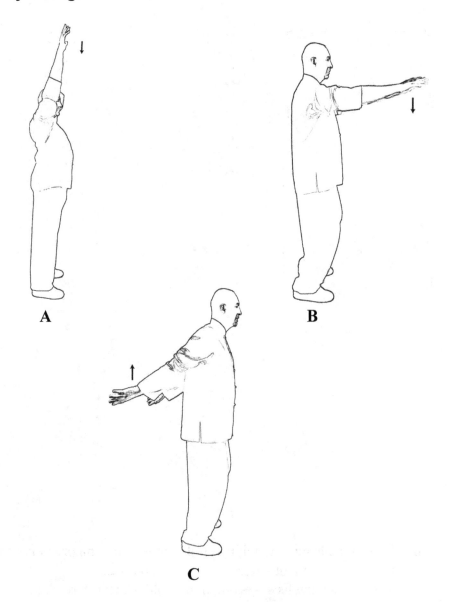

A

B

C

A, B, With the feet parallel and arms above the head, swing the arms
C down, sinking the knees at the same time. Let the whole body swing, keep the back straight and head upright. With your awareness, relax the shoulder and hips, elbows and knees, wrists and ankles, hands and feet. Do this for about 12 swings. This helps strengthen the whole body and is good for the blood circulation.

Swinging arms

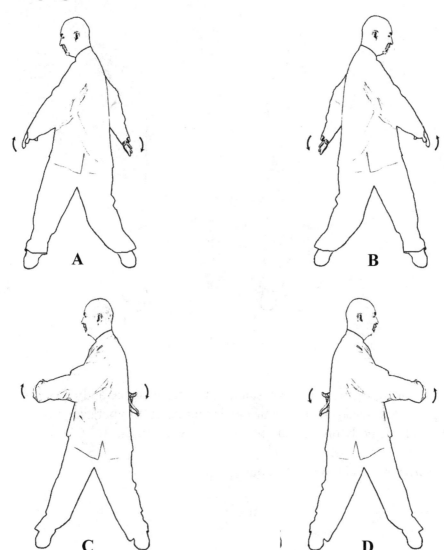

A, B Step out to a wider horse-riding stance. With the legs grounded firmly, the arms relaxed, let your arms swing out, turning from the waist. Let the arms slap across the body, massaging around the waist and hips.

C, D Let your arms swing higher, massaging around the kidneys and finally, still higher as one swinging arm taps the shoulder while the other taps the kidneys. Do this 12 times. This helps loosen and strengthen the back and helps massage the internal organs.

After the swinging exercises, stand in the basic stance and relax from the top of your head down to your hands and down to your feet, relax down through the body on the out breath for a few minutes.

We are now ready to practise our Qigong.

Chapter 5

Wudang Longevity

Taiji Hunyuan Zhuang Qigong

Absorbing the Essence

Wudang Longevity Qigong

The purpose of this Qigong practice is the stimulation of Qi around the Heavenly Orbit as described in Chapter Two, and the absorption of energy from our environment and the universe, described also in Chapter Two. Taoist Priest Grand Master Zhong Yunlong taught the Wudang Longevity practice to me in September 1999 at Wudang Mountain in China and has given me the authority to share its healing benefits.

It is best practised outdoors, looking into the distance.

Preparation

Stand with feet together, chin tucked in slightly and head held as though a silken cord is pulling your head towards the sky, lifting the spine. Place the tip of the tongue on the top palate of the mouth, just behind the front teeth. Lift the Hui Yin by gently squeezing the pelvic floor.

Breathe naturally in and out through the nose. Relax, letting the mind be clear.

Please note that the images are mirrored for the reader; just follow in the same direction.

Section 1

A
B

C

D

A, B As you open your eyes, sink down, bend the knees and step out to your left, setting the feet a bit wider than shoulder-width apart.

C Look to the distance and as you breathe in raise extended arms to the side of the body as if two balloons are lifting your arms, to about shoulder height. Hands are relaxed and the fingers are pointing to the ground (bringing the Qi up the back 'Du' channel).

D As you breathe out, turn the palms outward (Qi going to Lao Gong point in middle of palms). Breathe in, move arms up in a circle overhead, palms facing upwards (Qi going to Bai Hui point at top of head).

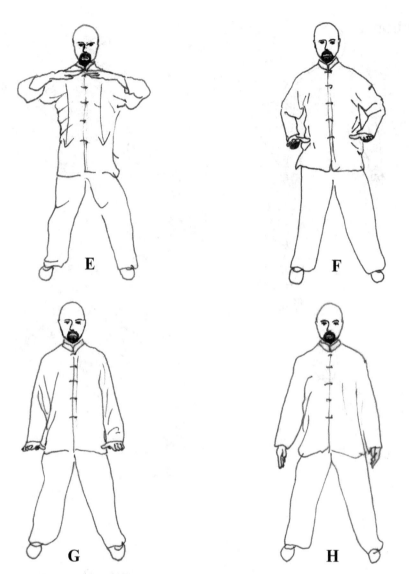

E Breathing out, turn palms down and bring them down in front of the body (Qi going down the front 'Ren' channel).

F When you reach navel height, breathe in and allow the thumbs to gently touch the body and follow around the waist to the sides, (Qi going around belt channel).

G Breathing out, push the palms down on the outside of the legs, fingers pointing to the front (Qi going down the outside of the legs).

H Pause for one breath and let the hands relax, fingers pointing down.

Repeat 3 times.

Section 2

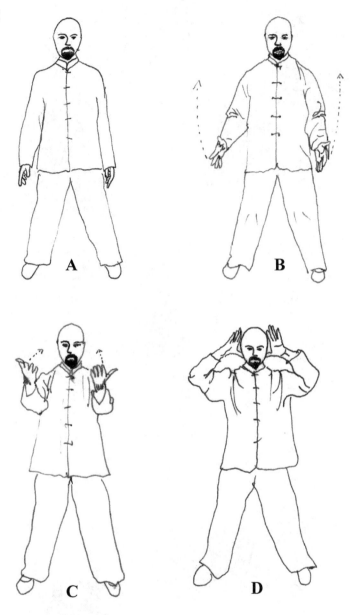

A Looking into the distance, breathe in.

B, C Raise the arms in front of the body to waist height. Breathe out as you turn the arms in a circle, scoop out in front.

D Breathing in, bring the hands back (bringing in the fresh Qi from the distance) around the ears (feeling the warmth of the hands).

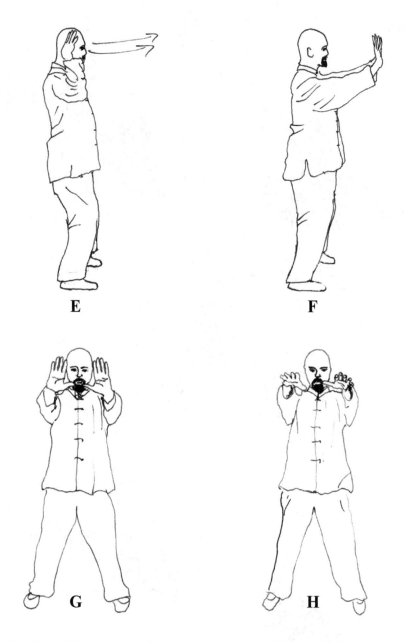

E, F, Breathing out, push arms out in front, like looking through a
G, H window, checking that arms are relaxed (letting stale Qi out).

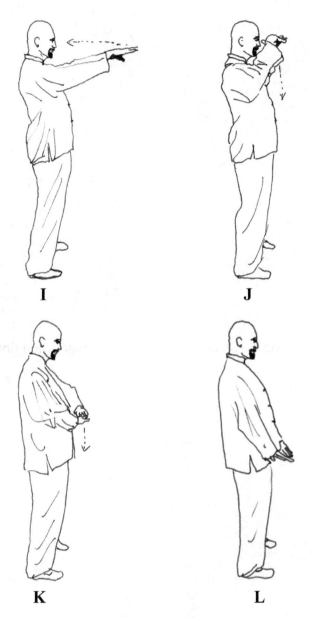

I   Breathing in, relax arms, and with the hands straight, bring them back toward the forehead.

J, K,   Breathing out and with palms facing down, bring the hands down
L   in front without touching the body.

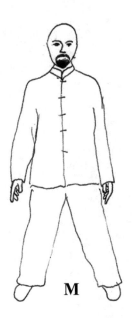

M

M   Pause with one breath and let hands relax, fingers pointing down.

Repeat 3 times.

Section 3(a)

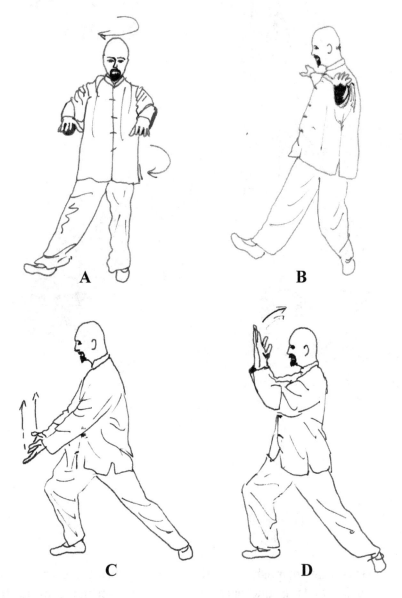

A, B   Looking into the distance, breathe in. Raise the arms in front of the body to waist height. Shift weight to your right leg and while pivoting on your left heel, turn the left foot out 90° to the side.

C, D   Breathing out, scoop the arms in a circle as you bring your weight forward over the left leg.

E   Breathing in, push from the front leg, bring the arms and body back, hands around ears as in Section 2 (bringing in the fresh Qi from distance).

F   Breathing out, push from back leg and push arms out in front like looking through a window as in Section 2 (letting stale Qi out).

G, H   Breathing in, push from the front leg and with arms and hands straight, bring them back to forehead height.

I   Breathing out, push from back leg and with palms turned down bring them down in front of the body, palms crossed, left hand on top, over the left knee.

Repeat 3 times to the left.

Section 3(b)

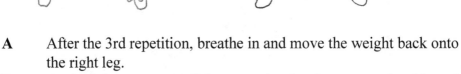

A   After the 3rd repetition, breathe in and move the weight back onto the right leg.

B   As the left toes come off the ground, raise the arms to the side and turn the body to face the front.

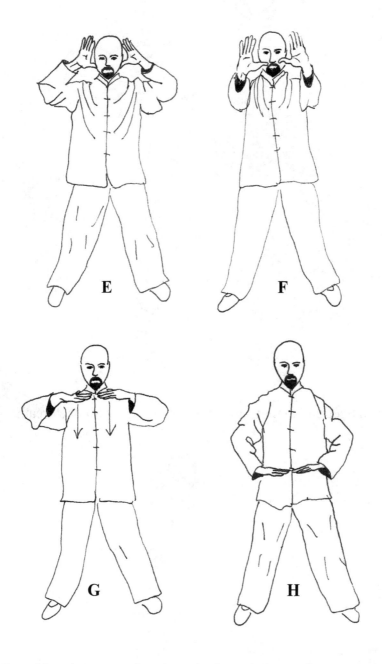

C-H Breathing out, scoop hands up in front and complete one
repetition to the front, as in Section 2, letting the arms rest by the
side with one breath.

I

I   As in Section 2, let the arms rest by the side with one breath.

Section 3(c) Now for the other side.

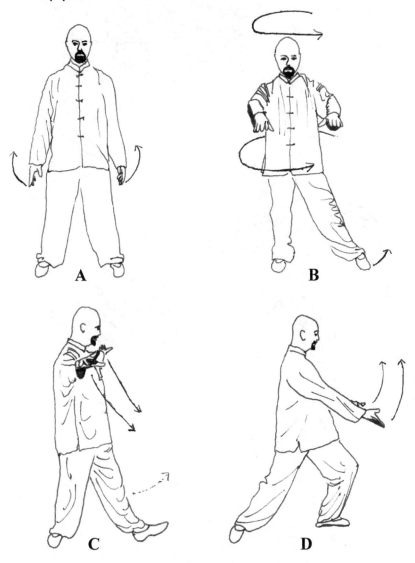

A, B,   On the next in breath raise the arms in front of the body,
C   shifting your weight to the left and pivoting on the right heel,
             turn the right foot out 90°.

D   Breathing out, scoop arms in front.

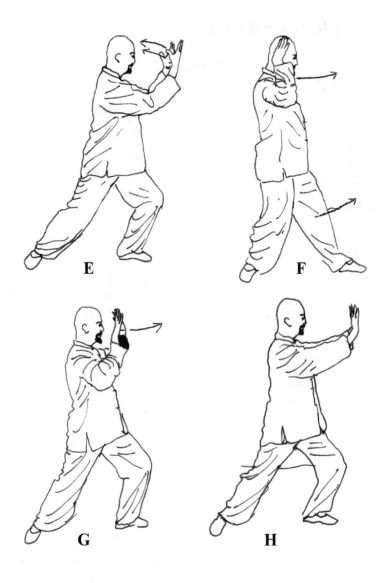

E   Breathing in, push from front leg bringing arms and body back, hands around ears as in previous section (bringing in the fresh Qi from distance).

F, G,   Breathing out, push from back leg, pushing arms out in front
H   (letting stale Qi out).

I   Breathing in, push from front leg, keeping arms and hand straight bring hands back to forehead height.

J, K   Breathing out, push from back leg and with palms facing down bring hands down in front of body, palms crossed with left hand still on top over the right knee.

L   On the next in breath raise the arms in front of the body, shifting your weight to the left and pivoting on the right heel, turn the foot and the body to face the front.

Repeat 3 times to the right.

Section 3(d)

A   After 3rd repetition breathe in, move weight back onto left leg. As
         the right toes come off the ground raise the arms to the side and
         turn the body to face the front.

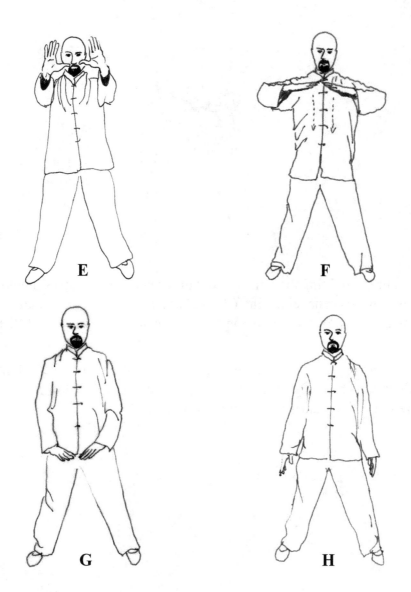

E

F

G

H

B-H   Breathe out; scoop hands up in front and complete one repetition
to the front, the same as in Section 2.

Closing

When finished, bring the arms in front of the body, palms up as if holding a big ball, hands at navel height. Check that the body is relaxed, chin tucked in. With the tip of the tongue on the top palate of the mouth, lift the Hui Yin.

Breathe naturally in and out through the nose. Relax and feel. Hold this position for a few minutes or for as long as feels comfortable. This position allows the Qi to gather at the Lower Dan Tian.

Final Closing

A, B   As you breathe in bring the arms up in a circular motion towards
the sky, beyond the clouds into the universe (absorbing the Qi).

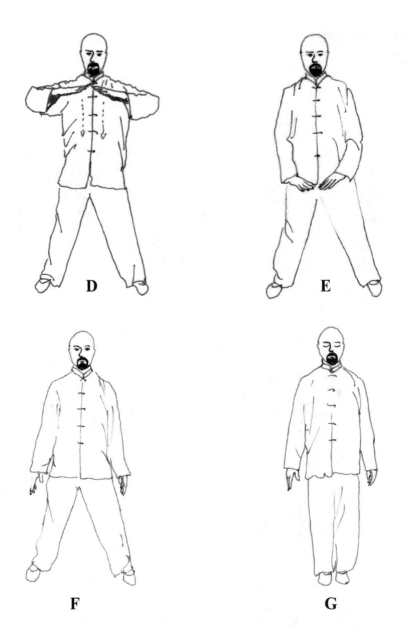

C, D, Breathe out, turn palms to face the forehead, allowing the
E heavenly Qi to flow down through the body like a shower of
energy through every cell, then turn palms facing down.

F, G Let the arms rest at the side of the body, move weight back to
your right bringing feet together again.

Chapter 6

Gathering the Qi
and Rubbing the Face

Absorbing the Essence

Gathering the Qi and Rubbing the Face

The practice of Qigong helps clear the energy channels and dredges the meridians of stagnant Qi. This allows the Qi to flow smoothly through the body and creates an energy or Qi field.

We generally feel this Qi field in the hands. To gather and refine the Qi move the hands in and out as follows:

Gathering the Qi

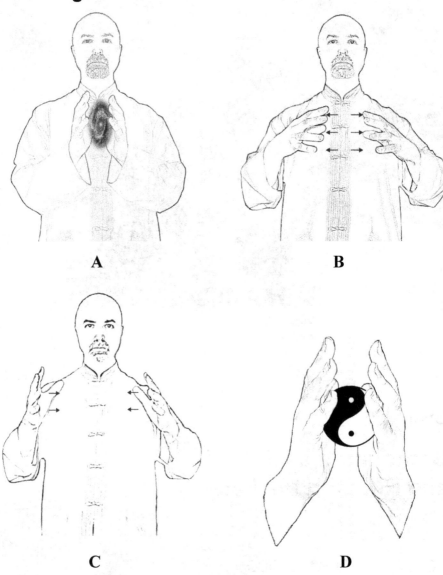

A

B

C

D

A Hold the hands in front of the body at chest height as if holding a ball of energy or light.

B Slightly draw the hands away from each other tensing the fingers.

C Then push the hands closer compressing the Qi between the hands.

Repeat six times.

D Relax and feel. We will generally feel warmth, like a field of energy between the hands. This creates a polarity as the left hand is Yang (positive) and the right hand is Yin (negative).

Now that the hands are charged with Qi it's a time for healing by placing the hands on a sore or injured part of our body or by massaging the face. Our face has many meridian acupuncture points that connect the meridians to the internal organs.

Face rubbing

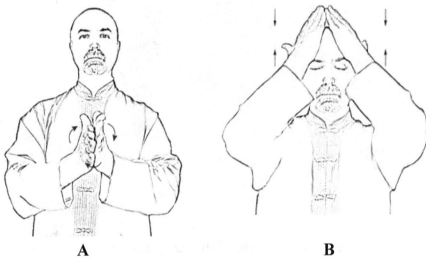

A   **B**

A Rub the hands together and bring the healing energy through your heart into your hands.

B Place the warm palms over your eyes (liver). Feel the warmth going in. Then rub the hands up and down from the forehead to the chin.

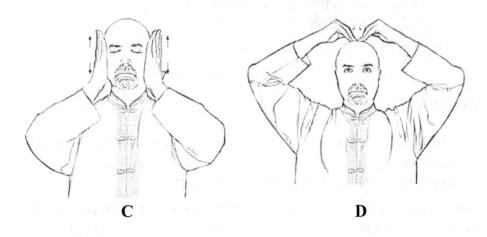

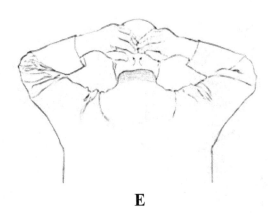

C   Rub the hands on the side of the face, then around the eyes and cheeks in a circular motion, like washing the face. Rub around the ears with the tip of the fingers massaging around the outside of the ears down to the ear lobe. With the tips of the fingers, massage around the inside of the ear following all the grooves, stimulating the kidneys.

D, E   With the tips of the fingers, massage back through the hair and then rub the back of the neck. Gently massage the base of the skull, the top of the head and massage up over the head and scalp.

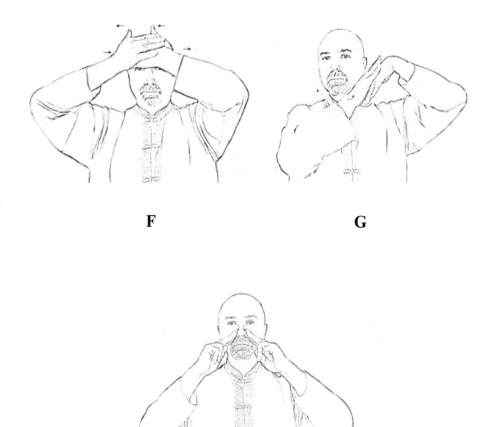

F   G

H

F, G,   With one hand on top of the other rub the palm across the
H   forehead and then rub around the chin letting the knuckles
massage the jaw. Rub the fingers down the sides of the nose and
around the cheek bones (lung).

Chapter 7

Ba Duan Jin - Eight Method Essence

Nurturing Life Qigong

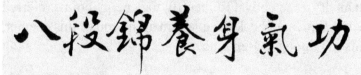

Absorbing the Essence

Ba Duan Jin - Eight Method Essence Nurturing Life Qigong

This ancient Qigong practice focuses on the circulation of Qi around the Heavenly Orbit. Grand Master Zhong Yunlong taught this practice to me in September 2000 at Wudang Mountain in China, a year after he taught me the Longevity form. He has given me the authority to share the healing benefits of these techniques with others.

Heavenly Orbit, also called the Micro Cosmic Orbit, is one of the foundation practices of Taoist cultivation of the human body. This approach views the body as a microcosmic representation of the universe. Our ultimate aim is to allow our internal energy to merge with the external, or macrocosmic energy.

The energy rising up the back of the body (Yang) merges with the energy descending down the front (Yin), creating a state of balance as shown in the Tai Chi symbol (Figure D). This practice concentrates on three main areas although many energy centres are located along this circuit.

The first is the Hui Yin, the convergence or meeting of the Yin, situated at the base of the body between the anus and genitals, also known as the perineum. We have already referred to this point in the Warm-up and Longevity form chapters, instructing you to 'lift the Hui Yin by gently squeezing the pelvic floor'.

The second area is the Bai Hui, which translates to '100 convergences', a point located at the top of the head at which Yang Qi gathers or meets.

The third, the Dan Tian, corresponds to the field where the elixir or energy grows. It is one of the major energy centres of the body and is situated just below the navel.

The orbit or circulation described by these points helps open and nourish all the energy channels of the body. [To identify the energy points referred to in these instructions, please check the diagram at the end of this chapter, 'Meditation Points in Qigong to Remember'.]

Preparation

This style of Qigong is done either sitting cross-legged on a cushion on the floor or sitting on the edge of a chair, keeping the back straight. Palms are placed down on the knees (Figure A or B).

The eyes are closed, the chin tucked in and head held as though a silken cord is pulling the head towards the sky. Place the tip of the tongue on the top palate of the mouth just behind the front teeth. Lift the Hui Yin. Breath naturally in and out through the nose; relax, letting the mind grow clear.

We meditate on the three energy centres for a few minutes starting with the Hui Yin, then the Bai Hui and lastly, the Dan Tian. Finally, with our awareness and breath, we thread these points together.

As you breathe in, allow the Qi to rise up the back along the 'Du' channel (Yang) from the Hui Yin point at the base of the body to the Bai Hui point at the top of the head. As you breathe out allow the Qi to descend along the 'Ren' channel (Yin) down the front of the body to the Dan Tian area below the navel. This breathing pattern, called **circulation breathing**, is done three times between each section of the sitting Ba Duan Jin.

Please note that the images are mirrored for the reader; just follow in the same direction.

Section 1. Dragon Biting Teeth

This exercise helps stimulates the 'Ren' channel and aids the digestive system.

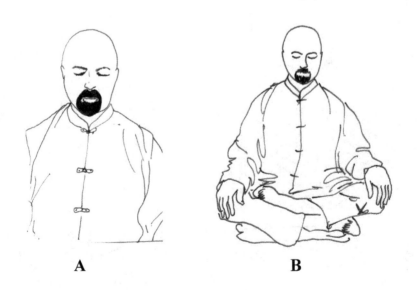

A   **B**

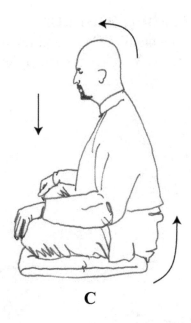

C

A   With the mouth closed, slowly clench the teeth, clearly and deliberately 36 times. Remember to practise gently, not too hard.

B   When finished, gather the Jade Nectar or saliva in the mouth and swallow once, meditatively, down to the Dan Tian. Relax and feel.

C   Take 3 circulation breaths.

Section 2.(1) Holding Kun Lun

Kun Lun is a sacred mountain in China and refers to the energy point at the back of the head, below Yu Chen (or Jade Pillow). This exercise helps stimulate the heart and the Du channel.

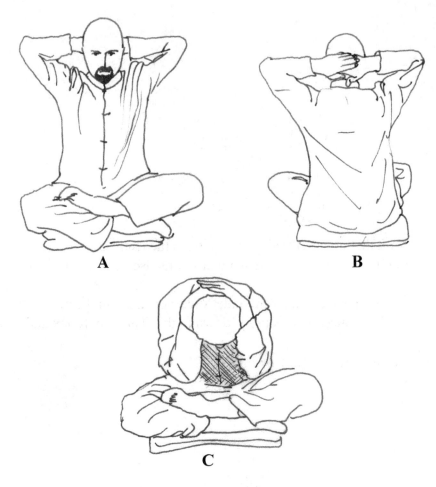

A, B   Breathe in, bring hands up to the Kun Lun and place one hand on top of the other (for males the left hand is on top, for females the right hand is on top) and at the same time bring the Qi to the Bai Hui point at the top of the head. Breathe out and send the Qi down to the Dan Tian.

C   Breathe in and on the out breath bring the elbows down in front of the body, keeping the back straight. Go as far as is comfortable.

Repeat 9 times.

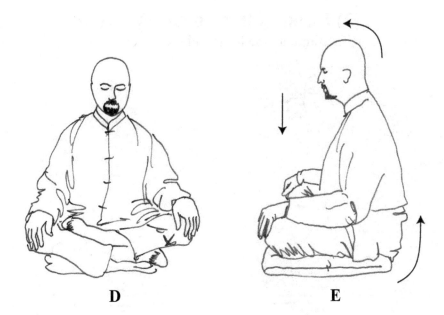

D   D

D   Place palms on knees. Relax and feel your inner state.

E   **Take 3 circulation breaths.**

Section 2.(2) Striking the Heavenly Drum

This exercise helps stimulate the heart and the Du channel.

A

B

C

D

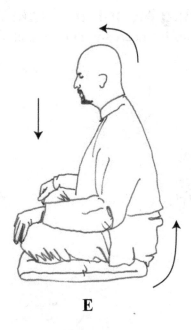

E

A, B   Breathe in and bring the hands up over the ears with the Lao Gong point in the palms of the hands over the ears, sealing in the air. At the same time take the Qi to the Bai Hui. Then breathe out, taking the Qi to the Dan Tian.

C   Drum the back of the head (Kun Lun) with the fingertips slowly, clearly and deliberately 24 times. There is no special breath – just breathe normally.

D   Place the palms on the knees. Relax and feel.

E   **Take 3 circulation breaths.**

Section 3. Pulling Mountain Peaks

This exercise stimulates the heart and Du channel.

A   B

C   D

E F

A   Breathe in, bring the hands to the back of the head (Kun Lun),
     as in section 2.1. At the same time take the Qi to the Bai Hui.
     Breathe out down to the Dan Tian, pause with one in-breath.

B   Breathe out, turn head to the left twisting the spine, taking care to
     only twist as far as comfortable.

C   Breathe in, rotating the body back to the front.

Repeat 24 times to the left.

D   Bring the palms onto the knees. Rest for a few breaths.

E   Repeat on the opposite (right) side 24 times.

When finished, place palms on knees. Relax and feel.

F   **Take 3 circulation breaths.**

Section 4. Golden Dragon Swimming in the Pool

This exercise stimulates the 'Ren' channel and aids the digestive system.

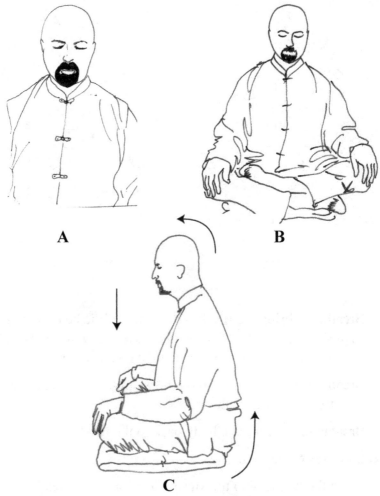

A

B

C

A   Rotate the tongue in one direction around the inside of the teeth in a circular motion on the inner gums, building up saliva or Jade Nectar (charged with Qi). Do this as many times as feels comfortable.

B   Then take one meditative swallow down to the Dan Tian. Repeat in the opposite direction.

Repeat in both directions twice with an equal number of rotations, clearly and deliberately, swallowing Jade Nectar down to the Dan Tian each time. Relax and feel.

C   **Take 3 circulation breaths.**

Section 5. Painting the Kidney House

This exercise helps stimulate the kidneys.

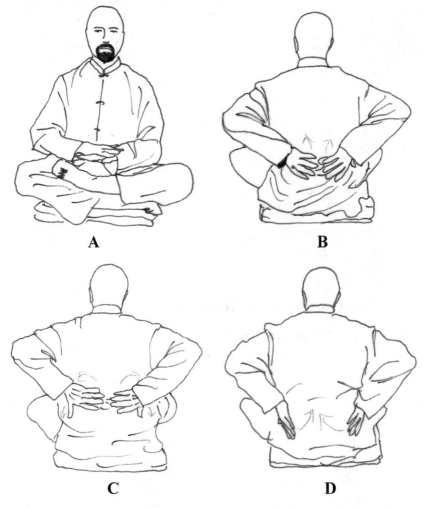

A

B

C

D

A   Rub the hands together with your top hand moving in a circle over the opposite palm, then turn over and repeat as many times as feels comfortable. (Imagine preparing a paint stick as in calligraphy, putting your loving kindness and energy into your hands.)

B   Place warm hands on the kidneys and let them absorb the warmth. Feel the kidneys.

C, D   Rub the palms up the spine and around the kidneys in a circular pattern, clearly and deliberately 36 times. Then allow the kidneys to absorb the warmth again.

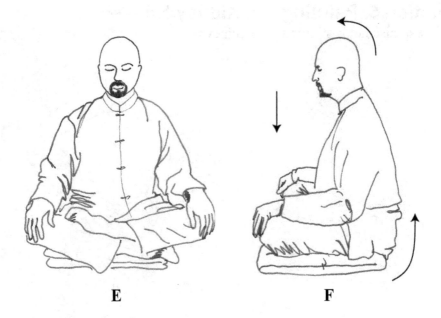

E   Place hands back on knees. Relax and feel.

F   Take 3 circulation breaths.

Section 6.(1) Turning Water Wheel both sides

This exercise helps stimulate the five Yin organs – heart, spleen, lungs, kidneys and liver.

A

B

C

D side

A   Place both palms face up at the Dan Tian.

B, C   Breathe in, bring the right hand to chest height, then circle out in front looking across fingertips.

D   Breathing out, the hand goes down in a circle then up again (like turning a wheel).

Repeat 9 times.

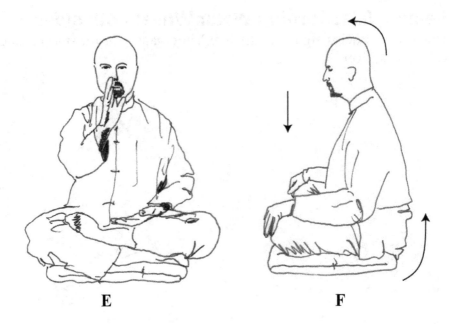

E   Pause for a few breaths then repeat with the left hand 9 times.

When breathing in, bring the Qi up the back to the Kun Lun point. When breathing out, take the Qi down the arm, out to the fingertips.

F   Place hands back on knees. Relax and feel.

F   **Take 3 circulation breaths.**

Section 6.(2) Turning Water Wheel double hands

This stimulates the five Yin organs.

A

B

C

A   Place palms face up at the Dan Tian. Breathe in and bring both hands up to chest height.

B, C Breathe out, bring hands around in a circle as in section 6.1. Pause for a breath in between, allowing the Qi to circulate once.

Repeat 9 times.

Again, when breathing in, bring the Qi up the back to the Kun Lun point and when breathing out, move the Qi down the arms to the hands and fingers.

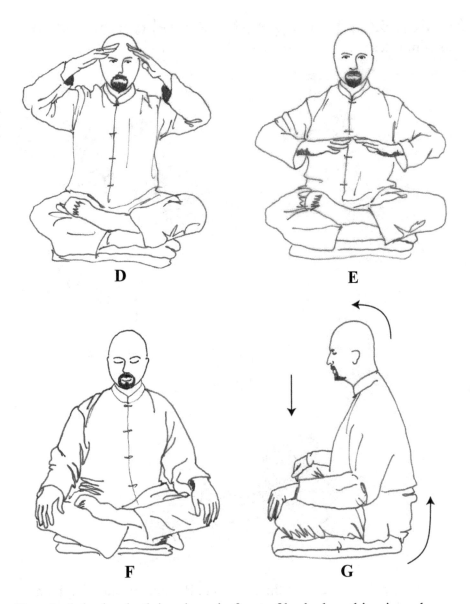

D

E

F

G

Close by bringing both hands up in front of body, breathing in, palms facing up (as in Figure A).

D, E   Then turn palms down in front of face and push down in front of your body, breathing out.

F   Let hands rest on knees. Relax and feel.

G   **Take 3 circulation breaths.**

Section 7. Tapping the Roof

This exercise helps to stimulate Qi through all the channels.

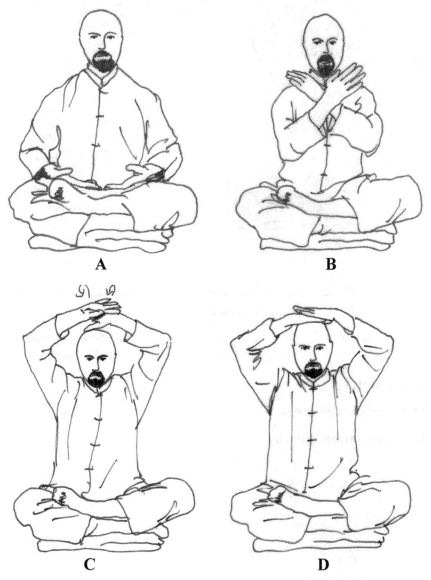

A, B Breathe in, raise both hands up in front of face in a circular motion.

C, D Breathe out, turning palms over the top of head, left hand on top
for males, right hand on top for females, then bring the palms
solidly down on top of head, 'tapping the roof'.

Repeat tapping 9 times.

| E | F |

E   Pull both hands up at the same time. Breathe in, bringing the Qi up the back to the top of head.

F   Breathe out, bring hands down front of body, bring Qi down to Dan Tian, place hands on knees, pause for a few breaths.

Repeat 3 times

Return hands to the knees. Relax and feel.

Take 3 circulation breaths.

Section 8. Dragon Resting on the Bottom of the Sea

This exercise will help to stimulate Qi down and up the legs.

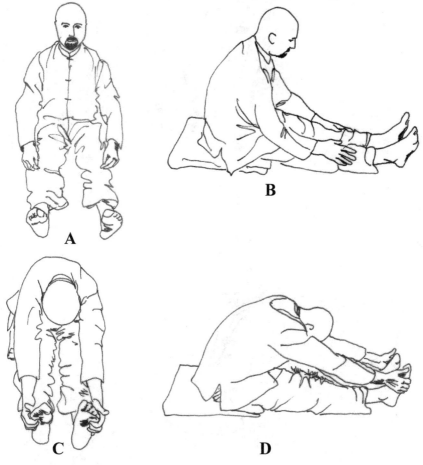

A   If you're sitting on the floor, place both legs straight out in front, slowly. With the finger tips, massage the Ju San Li point on the outside of the legs, four fingers' width down from the knee cap.

B, C,   Stretch down both hands touching the legs and grabing the
D   outside of both feet. With the fingers, grasp Yong Chuan (gushing springs) then raise the torso, not touching the legs.

Repeat this stretch 12 times.

If sitting on a chair, place the legs out in front with the heels on the ground and the toes pulled back. Massage the stomach point as above, and then bend forward stretching down, touching the legs as far as comfortable but not touching the legs when coming back up. Repeat 12 times.

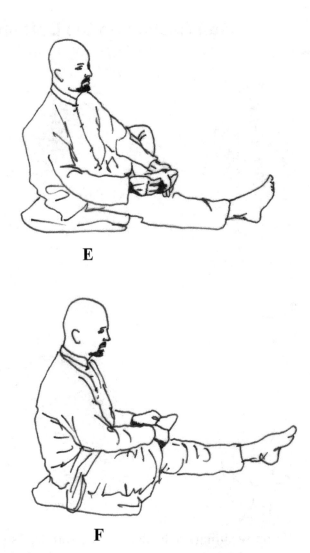

E

F

E, F   Finish by rubbing the Yong Chuan point on the sole of each foot.

Then bring the legs back to the meditation position, hands on knees. Relax and feel.

Take 3 circulation breaths.

When finished, we enter a quiet, peaceful space and meditate for as long as feels comfortable. Allow your Qi to merge with the universe, returning to nothingness.

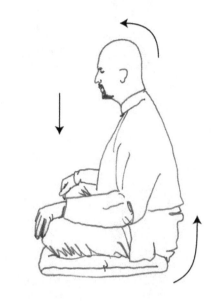

Chapter 8

Qigong Meditation Heavenly Orbit

Absorbing the Essence

The Qigong Meditation - Heavenly Orbit

Qigong meditation is also known as Nei Gong, meaning internal work or skill. Qigong Grand Master Jack Lim first taught this practice to me in 1994. He explained to me the importance of the flow of Qi around the energy circuit of the body and how this flow of Qi ultimately connects with everything in our universe. Jack taught me many things and helped me understand the connection to and natural flow of the Qi energy. When I first met Jack, I was already a full-time Tai Chi teacher and found his methods were very different to those of my previous teachers. When I asked how I should teach or structure the Qigong forms that he had taught me, he would answer, "It's up to you. I'm not going to tell you what to teach each week but first of all, make sure the students understand and can feel the Qi."

When I started teaching Jack's style of Qigong in 1996, the only direct instruction he had given me regarding teaching was to incorporate meditation into the class and to teach the Heavenly Orbit Qigong Meditation. Jack continued to help me develop this practice and I released a Qigong Meditation CD in the year 2000. There are a few different approaches to this meditation but they are all based on the same principle, the opening of the extraordinary meridians of the body. The Du (Yang) channel rises up the back and nourishes all the Yang meridians of the body and the Ren (Yin) channel descends down the front of the body, nourishing all the Yin meridians. The following meditation may seem fairly technical at first but with regular practice it will soon feel quite natural.

Preparation

Begin by sitting cross-legged on a cushion on the floor or on the edge of a chair, keeping the back straight. Rest your hands in your lap, palms facing up, right hand on top for females, left hand on top for males.

Sit with eyes closed, chin tucked in and head held as though a silken cord is pulling the head towards the sky. Relax your shoulders and place the tip of your tongue on the top palate of the mouth just behind the front teeth. Lift the Hui Yin by gently squeezing the pelvic floor. Breath naturally in and out through the nose and relax, letting the mind be clear.

Use your awareness to concentrate on the energy centres around the Heavenly Orbit. A basic principle in Qigong maintains that where the mind goes, the Qi will follow. The Qi flows naturally around this orbit and our job is to strengthen this flow. It's important not to try too hard, but to relax and feel each energy point described below. If you feel distracted, use your breathing to focus the mind. As you bring your attention to each point, relax and feel, and concentrate on this location for six breaths.

1. Ming Men or Door to Life – situated on the spine at the back of the body directly behind the navel.

2. Yu Zhen or Jade Pillow – at the base of the skull.

3. Bai Hui or Hundred Points Converge – found at the top of the head.

4. Upper Dan Tian or Upper Centre of Energy – the spot between the eyebrows. As you relax, let your eyes rest.

5. Middle Dan Tian or Middle Centre of Energy – at the middle of the chest in the chest cavity.

6. Dan Tian or Centre of Energy – the area beneath the navel.

7. Hui Yin or Convergence of Yin Energy – situated at the base of the body between anus and the genitals, also known as the perineum.

From the Hui Yin, the Qi flows down the outside of the legs, and we concentrate on the outside of the knees, then the outside of the ankles. Continue into the feet, relaxing the toes, each row of joints, row by row, like water slowly flowing down to the tip of the toes. Relax and feel or concentrate on this area for six breaths, feeling the peace at the tip of the toes.

8. Yong Chuan or Gushing Springs – on the souls of the feet.

The Qi flows from the Yong Chuan up the inside of the legs around the ankles to the inside of the knees and back to the Hui Yin. Again, relax and feel at this point for six breaths.

9. Chang Qiang or End of Spine – just beneath the coccyx at the base of the spine.

10. Return to the Ming Men or Door to Life – on the spine at the back of the body directly behind the navel.

11. Stop again at the Yu Zhen or Jade Pillow – at the base of the skull.

From the Jade Pillow the Qi flows across the shoulders, down the inside of the arms. We concentrate on the elbows, then the wrists.

12. Lao Gong or Palace of Labour – in the middle of the palms of the hands. Move down to the tips of your fingers, relaxing each finger, each row of joints, row by row, like water slowly flowing down to the tips of the fingers. Relax and feel, focus six breaths into this area, feeling the peace at the tips of the fingers.

The Qi flows from the Lao Gong around the outside of the hands to the wrists, to the elbows and then to the shoulders and back to . . .
13. Jade Pillow – at the base of the skull.

14. Bai Hui or Hundred Points Converge – at the top of the head.

15. Upper Dan Tian or Upper Centre of Energy – the spot between the eyebrows, resting the eyes again.

16. Middle Dan Tian or Middle Centre of Energy – the area in the middle of the chest in the chest cavity.

17. Dan Tian or Centre of Energy – the area beneath the navel.

Closing
Turn the palms in over the Dan Tian, feeling the warmth. Begin tracing circles around the Dan Tian as if turning a wheel, 36 times, starting with small circles, gradually getting larger. When finished, the hands should be on the upper chest. Turn the hands over, reversing them, and again trace circles in the opposite direction 24 times, large to small, finishing with hands resting on the Dan Tian. The number nine represents Yang. Four nines equal 36, or Yang expanding. The number six represents Yin. Four sixes equal 24, or Yin contracting.

When performing this exercise, the hands just touch the surface of the skin or clothes. Start slowly and increase the speed to a medium pace. Keep this pace when going back in the opposite direction and finish slowly.

It is also important that women start in a counter clockwise direction (Yin) and men in a clockwise direction (Yang).

When finished, rub the hands together. Place these warm healing hands over your eyes, feeling the warmth going in. Then rub the hands up and down from the forehead to the chin, then the side of the face up and down, around the eyes and cheeks in a circular motion, like washing the face. Rub around the ears with the tips of the fingers, massaging around the outside of the ears down to the ear lobe. With the tips of the fingers, massage around the inside of the ear following all the grooves, stimulating the blood and Qi. With the tips of the fingers, comb backward through the hair and rub the back of the neck. Massage the back of the neck up to the base of the skull, the Jade Pillow point. At the top of head or Bui Hui, massage the head and scalp. With the palms together, rub across the forehead and then, with one hand on top of the other, rub around the chin letting the knuckles massage the jaw. With your fingers, rub down the side of the nose to under the cheek bone.

Finally, place the palms down on the knees for a few minutes, sensing the peace, the inner peace, the nothingness.

Meditation Points

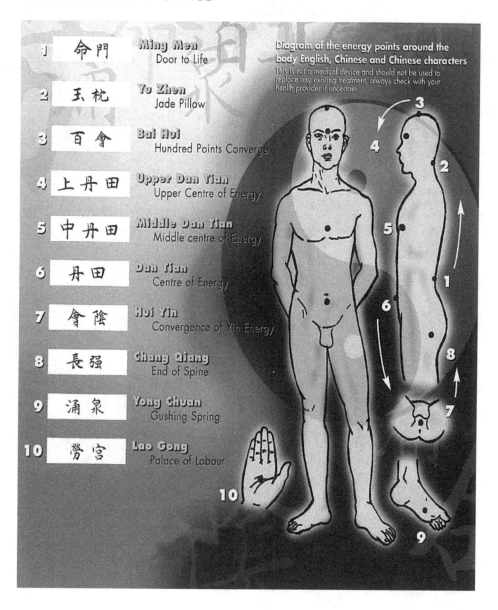

#	Chinese	Name	English
1	命門	Ming Men	Door to Life
2	玉枕	Yu Zhen	Jade Pillow
3	百會	Bai Hui	Hundred Points Converge
4	上丹田	Upper Dan Tian	Upper Centre of Energy
5	中丹田	Middle Dan Tian	Middle centre of Energy
6	丹田	Dan Tian	Centre of Energy
7	會陰	Hui Yin	Convergence of Yin Energy
8	長強	Chang Qiang	End of Spine
9	涌泉	Yong Chuan	Gushing Spring
10	勞宮	Lao Gong	Palace of Labour

Diagram of the energy points around the body English, Chinese and Chinese characters

This is not a medical device and should not be used to replace any existing treatment, always check with your health provider if uncertain

Chapter 9

Stories to Inspire

Absorbing the Essence

Stories to Inspire

It was about two years ago that I came across Qigong for the first time and I find it's all great fun. However, I have a serious purpose. A couple of years ago I injured myself fixing a compost bin and gradually recovered but I found the gentle flowing movements of Qigong together with its strong spiritual base, particularly welcome.

I now have neck injuries as a result of digging the garden plus a lot of personal stress, now resolved. The physiotherapist is marvellous, my gym instructor is easing me into helpful exercises, and I've signed up for a rehabilitation course BUT I find the healing effects of Qigong and the sense of wellbeing and peace that it provides, are second-to-none.

Qigong is a daily (early morning) delight and I just love the quaint titles – 8 pieces of brocade, painting the kidney house, turning mountain peaks etc.

I hesitate to admit my age – 82! However, the good news is that apart from my current anatomical hiccough (which I'm determined is only temporary) I am lucky enough to enjoy excellent health. I am looking forward to receiving the two CDs I ordered to add to my collection. What a feast!
Edith Levin, New Zealand

I have sent some of your DVDs and CDs to friends as gifts. They were very appreciative and have all been given some physical and mental relief as they practised your Qigong movements and some have discovered the gentle healing of your meditation CDs.

Three years ago I was attacked on my morning walk. (I am a small woman aged 82 years). What followed were months of pain and an inability to walk more than 50 metres. A dear friend of mine who practised Qigong with Simon and is a healer, treated me and gave me some relief from pain. She left a parcel for me that I opened a few days later and found your DVD 'Absorbing the Essence'.

The first time I watched it I knew my injured body could manage the exquisite, slow movements of Qigong. I practised each morning and after two weeks the pain had gone from my back (still badly bruised). In another month I was able to walk freely! How lovely!

So everything moved along smoothly and I was completely at ease with myself, until… eight months later I was walking along on the floor a one metre wide balcony and did not notice a thick commercial rug. The toe of my shoe caught in it and I was thrown into the air and landed on my right shoulder on concrete.

I spent six weeks in hospital and now have a metal rod in my upper arm and a metal ball in my shoulder plus back problems. Nevertheless, I could not put Qigong aside completely as I yearned for that feeling of wellbeing I had previously achieved. I used to lie on my bed and do the Qigong movements in my thoughts. I called it phantom Qigong – this amused the doctors.

I was at home for four months before I could raise my right arm enough to practise. Each day I kept trying. Gradually my movements began to flow more freely. Now, 11 months later, I am once again reaping the benefits of Qigong and am quite strong again.
Elva Madden, NSW

A fortunate coincidence of instinct and opportunity led me to join my first Tai Chi class approximately 20 years ago. My first Tai Chi teacher was very skilled in the martial arts aspect of Tai Chi yet I yearned to develop the spiritual, meditative and healing side of this ancient Eastern practice. I felt very blessed when I chanced upon Simon's demonstration lesson and open class in Centennial Park in the same year.

I once again trusted my instinct and joined Simon's fledgling Qigong class. The constant nourishment that Qigong provides for me on so many levels has meant that I have seldom missed a class and I now go to three classes a week.

While the class is in progress, my worrying thoughts and problems are put on the backburner and even seem to graciously dissolve and disappear into the atmosphere, not returning with the same intensity once class is over. And at the end of each class, everyone is smiling – a true, honest, gentle smile from the core of each soul – and no one wants to leave the comfort of the closing meditation circle.

Now when I do art and craft work, I have discovered my breath and hands often become one, and it is of interest to note that the warm-up toning exercises of artists, calligraphers, musicians, athletes etc. are often based on simple yet universal Qigong principles.

Under stress, the practice, thought or even memory of a Qigong movement will circulate my energy favourably around my body and I relax knowing that the Qigong system is sending its circulation and breath to the vital organs and 'right parts' and that I can trust myself and my body to help heal itself. With Qigong, the most gentle and subtle movements promote and provide the most substantial, profound and enduring effects.

Susan Lenn, NSW

Qigong has been a part of my life for about six years. I usually practice about four times a week. When I started to learn Tai Chi, Qigong was included as part of the class. When the opportunity came up to attend a Qigong workshop I jumped at the chance, and have been practising, teaching and attending workshops ever since.

For me, Qigong is about energy flow. By practising Qigong movements, combined with deep breathing and intention, one can enhance the flow of healing energy through the body. By having the intention to cultivate Qi in the body we can improve our sense of wellbeing and health. Practising Qigong makes me feel relaxed and peaceful. I focus only on what I am doing and can feel the flow of energy through my body. Being familiar with the movements (so I do't have to think about what comes next or how to do the movement) means that I can get into a flowing, rhythmic, meditative state with a totally relaxed body and mind. It is this state that really allows me to gain the most benefit from Qigong. This makes all the practice and learning I had to do to reach this point all worthwhile.

I have found Qigong meditation particularly powerful and feel that I have the ability to direct healing energy to particular parts of my body with my intention. I use this ability as an adjunct to my healing when receiving Bowen Therapy.

I have learnt that life is not what it seems on the surface and that there are powerful healing energies available to us if we seek them out and dedicate ourselves to cultivating out ability to use the universal Qi to improve our health and wellbeing. I have also learnt that I feel a natural affinity with the practices of Qigong, Tai Chi and meditation. Practicing and cultivating Qi has greatly enhanced my life.

As a Qigong instructor/teacher I am fascinated by the different experiences people seem to have when they begin their own Qigong journey. I have observed that those who open their minds to the possibilities that Qigong offers get far more out of the practice than those who just come along for a bit of gentle exercise or a social outing. Some can feel the energy flowing right away and are able to connect with themselves – even to the point of experiencing the emotion some movements can bring up.

Generally though, I have found that if participants come regularly to classes for about six months, they become 'hooked' and really feel that the Qigong is benefiting them. Some only experience benefit on the physical level (greater flexibility and range of movement), but all enjoy the opportunity to relax and flow with the universal energy, even if they wouldn't describe it as this.

Jay McGough, VIC

I have been learning Qigong with Master Simon Blow for three years and I practise regularly at least five times per week. I first started practising Tai Chi Chuan ten years ago and had my first experience of Qigong doing the Shibashi form. I realised that for me the Qigong was a more effective exercise for achieving better health, and an awareness of the Qi flow through my body. It is amazing that after only a few lessons one can actually feel the Qi – then you know you are doing something very beneficial for your body and the health of your internal organs.

Often at the start of practice my mind is racing and busy. Sometimes during practice I feel the energy running through my body. I get hot after doing some of the Ba Duan Jin, and even at times feel myself swaying with the movement of Qi. At the finish of the practice I am calm, my mind is focused and I am aware that my whole body feels connected and energised.

I feel that my health is stronger, and I am more aware of my energy levels, especially when I am working. When I practise my Qigong in the evening I sleep so much better, therefore I have more energy the next day.

I have learnt that it takes dedication to practise regularly if you are doing it on your own. I have found that as soon as I start my practice, my mind and body go to another place – as if connected to the Qi energy of the universe. When I finish my practice – usually at least 30-60 minutes – I feel good in myself. I believe my practice is helping me overcome my habit of procrastination.

I enjoy learning Qigong practice with a Master like Simon Blow. He has a wonderful style of teaching, the instruction is clear and informative, his enthusiasm is contagious and he is always calm. This has enabled me to learn at my own pace and I can view his DVDs to refine my own form and practice at home. I have also joined Simon at his retreats at Sunnataram Forest Monastery, and the experience is quite unique with a mixture of Qigong practice and meditation. I recommend it to anyone practising Qigong.

I also travelled with Master Simon Blow to China in April 2009. Simon as our leader gave generously of his time each day for one hour of practice every morning to start each day. Travelling in China with a wonderful group of likeminded people has expanded my appreciation of all Qigong practice. Meeting Dr Xu in Xiyuan Hospital in Beijing and doing the 'Guigen' with him in the gardens was a powerful experience. The mystical mountains of Wudangshan, with Temples and Monasteries shrouded in wispy clouds, was magical.

Our visit to the Eternal Spring Temple for Taoist studies was memorable. The Master inspired us with stories of his life and his personal development of Qi, and under his guidance during a standing meditation he used his Qi to enhance our experience of our own Qi. The Bullet Train reached 262 km/h on our journey to Shanghai where we shopped till we dropped, and visited Shanghai University for another perspective on Qigong. We then said goodbye to new friends – our China tour was at its end.
Cherel Waters, NSW

I first started doing Tai Chi about 15 years ago and after a number of years moved to Qigong. I don't practise the movements every week. I do my best to practise some aspects only – breathing and stretching on a daily basis. I enjoyed working with Simon and was reaping the benefits of Tai Chi so when he started classes close to home with Qigong I decided to go along and learn more about it.

Qigong makes me feel awesome. After a Qigong class I have more clarity and peace of mind. It renews my energy and assists with the stresses of work. I find it most effective in the mornings. It gives me an opportunity to invest time in my health and spiritual development, and gain and maintain a centredness and calm mind in times of stress.

Simon is an inspirational Master. His instructions are clear, making each class an enjoyable, learning experience. He has a real strength of presence and connection. I have learnt (and I continue to enjoy learning) not only the movements of Qigong but also to apply the philosophy and principles into my life – thank you Simon. Simon's Qigong study tours to China were a real eye-opener, a fantastic opportunity to explore the culture of China while learning from our Masters (and students) alike. Simon's tours offer exceptional value for money. The whole experience of learning and practising not only the techniques, but incorporating the philosophy and other aspects of Qigong have been fantastic. The health benefits are obvious, not only physically but also spiritually and mentally.

Debbie Edwards, NSW

I started Tai Chi/Qigong in the late '80s. The Qigong aspect became my focus more and more over the years. I practise daily in some way or another.

I had a neck and back injury from childhood and wanted something I could do for the rest of my life that was wholistic. I was attracted to it because I loved karate but saw Qigong as a complete lifestyle for me. Qigong to me is working with the fabric of life and connecting with the life force. It's like the Tao – if it is spoken it is not the Tao. Qigong is part of my life. It enhances everything I do on all levels – body, mind and spirit.

Doing Qigong has made me more patient, calm, tolerant and compassionate. I feel empowered being able to look after my own health. I heal quickly if I do get unwell. Qigong has given me another view of life. I have learnt that I need open spaces and I appreciate fresh air and life itself more profoundly.

Over these past 20 years Qigong has become the basis of the way I view life, so much so that when choosing our new home I was looking for a special place where the Qi was strong and energising. We have moved into a wonderful property with a lake/dam, fresh air, and quiet with plenty of nature around us. I have been teaching Tai Chi/Qigong for 20 years and look forward to running classes and workshops here so many others can also enjoy the beautiful Qi that's here.

Diana Schmidt, NSW

CDs – by Simon Blow

CD1: Five Elements Qigong Meditation

This CD is the perfect introduction to Qigong meditation (Neigong). **Track one** features a 30-minute heart-felt guided meditation to help bring love and light from the universe into your body. It harmonises the Five Elements – Fire, Earth, Metal, Water and Wood – with the corresponding organs of the body, respectively the heart, spleen, lungs, kidney and liver. This is one of the foundations of Chinese Qigong. Let Qigong Master Simon Blow help harmonise the elements of the universe with the energy of your body by using colour and positive images. **Track two** provides 30 minutes of relaxing music by inspiring composer Dale Nougher.

CD2: Heavenly Orbit Qigong Meditation

This CD is intended for the intermediate student. **Track one** takes you through a 30-minute guided meditation using your awareness to stimulate the energy centres around the body and open all the meridians. The circulation of Qi (Chi) around the Heavenly Orbit is one of the foundations of Chinese Qigong. The energy rising up the back 'Du' channel harmonises with the energy descending down the front 'Ren' channel, helping balance the energy of the body. Master Simon Blow guides you to open the energy centres of your own body to create harmony with the universe. **Track two** provides 30 minutes of relaxing music by Dale Nougher.

CD3: Return to Nothingness Qigong Meditation

This CD is intended for the advanced student and those wanting a healing night-practice. One of the aims of Qigong is to allow our internal energy (Qi) to harmonise with the external energy (Qi) allowing our consciousness to merge with the universe. When we enter into a deep sleep or meditation all the meridians start to open and much healing can take place. In this 20-minute guided meditation Simon Blow assists you in guiding your energy through your body and harmonising with the energy of the universe. Track two provides 30 minutes of healing music by Dale Nougher.

Sleep

Sleep is necessary to maintain life, alongside breathing, eating, drinking, and exercising of the mind and body. Without a good six to eight hours of sleep each night it can be hard to live a quality, balanced, fulfilling life. When we sleep it's a time to rest and rejuvenate the mind and body and to release the physical, mental and emotional stress that has built up during the day. This also helps uplift us spiritually.

It's a time to rest; it's time for a good night's sleep. Let Simon Blow's soothing voice, along with Dale Nougher's beautiful piano music and the natural sounds of the ocean, help guide you to release the tension of the day and enable you to enter a deep, fulfilling sleep.

Book/DVD sets – by Simon Blow

"About 18 months ago I started to practise Qigong as I knew that it would improve my health. I needed to do it regularly, ideally every day, but being in a rural area presented logistical problems. I discovered Simon's DVD and commenced daily practice. The great advantage for me was that I didn't have to travel to classes and could do them whenever I felt like it. Since that time I have noticed great improvement in my overall wellbeing. It has helped me to reinvent my clinical practice as a holistic massage practitioner. A number of my clients now have Simon's DVD and I feel this is helping them to both improve their health and well being, and to empower themselves." **Robin Godson-King (Holistic Massage Practitioner)**

(Each set contains a DVD plus a book that provides diagrams and instructions for the movements contained on the DVD. The book also includes interesting reading about the practice of Qigong as well as inspirational stories.)

The Art of Life

'The Art of Life' presents the Qigong styles that were taught to me in Australia: the Taiji Qigong Shibashi, which I learned as an instructor with the Australian Academy of Tai Chi from 1990 to 1995; and the Ba Duan Jin standing form, commonly known as the Eight Pieces of Brocade, taught to me in 1996 by Sifu John Dolic in Sydney.

This is the perfect introduction to this ancient art and is suitable for new and continuing students of all ages. The book follows the DVD and contains three sections: **1. Warm up** – gentle movements loosen all the major joints of the body, lubricating the tendons and helping increase blood and energy circulation. It is beneficial for most arthritic conditions; **2. Ba Duan Jin or Eight Pieces of Brocade** – this is the best known and most widely practised form of Qigong throughout the world, also known as Daoist Yoga. The movements stretch all the major muscles, massage organs and open the meridians of the body; **3. Taiji Qigong Shibashi** – this popular practice is made up of eighteen flowing movements. The gentle movements harmonise the mind, body and breath. Total running time: 55 minutes.

"Tai Chi Qigong is a gentle way of exercising the whole body and provides long-term benefits. I recommend it to my patients as an effective way of improving muscle tone and joint mobility. Those who practise regularly have fewer problems with their muscles and joints and often report an increased sense of health and wellbeing. This is an excellent video with clear and simple instruction."
Roman Maslak. B.A. (Hons), D.O. Osteopath

Absorbing the Essence

'Absorbing the Essence' comprises the Qigong cultivation techniques that were taught to me by Grand Master Zhong Yunlong in 1999 and 2000 at Wudangshan or Wudang Mountain. Wudang is one of the sacred Daoist Mountains of China and is renowned for the development of Taiji.

This DVD and book is for the intermediate student and for people with experience in meditation. It contains three sections: **1. Warm up** – the same as in The Art of Life DVD; **2. Wudang Longevity Qigong** – this sequence of gentle, flowing movements stimulates the Heavenly Orbit, absorbing the primordial energy from the environment and letting the negativity dissolve into the distance; **3. Sitting Ba Duan Jin** – this 30-minute sequence includes eight sections with exercises to stimulate different organs and meridians of the body. It is practised in a seated position on a chair or cushion – ideal for people who have discomfort whilst standing. These practices originated from the famous Purple Cloud Monastery at the sacred Wudang Mountain in China. Total running time: 60 minutes.

"Simon Blow of Australia has twice travelled (1999, 2000) to Mt Wudang Shan Daoist Wushu College to learn Taiji Hunyuan Zhuang (Longevity) Qigong and Badajin Nurturing Life Qigong and through his study has absorbed the essence of these teachings. Therefore, I specially grant Simon the authority to teach these, spreading the knowledge of these Qigong methods he has learnt at Mt Wudang to contribute to the wellbeing of the human race. May the Meritorious Deeds Be Infinite."
Grand Master Zhong Yunlong, Daoist Priest and Director,
Mt Wudang Shan Taoist Wushu College, China, September 24, 2000.

Restoring Natural Harmony

Chinese Medical Qigong

Qigong

Book / DVD No.3

Simon Blow

Restoring Natural Harmony

This DVD and book is for the advanced student or for the person wanting to learn specific Traditional Chinese Medicine self-healing exercises. Each section works on a different organ meridian system of the body – Spleen, Lungs, Kidney, Liver and Heart – which relate to the Five Elements – Earth, Metal, Water, Wood and Fire. Guigen Qigong originated from Dr Xu Hongtao, a Qigong Specialist Doctor from the Xiyuan Hospital in Beijing. These internal exercises help regulate the meridian system bringing harmony to mind, body and spirit. Total running time: 75 minutes.

"Simon Blow first visited our hospital in 2002. I was impressed with his knowledge and commitment to Qigong. He returned in 2004 to study Chinese Medical Qigong. Simon is a gifted teacher: he has the rare ability to inspire others and impart to them the healing benefits of Qigong."
Dr Xu Hongtao, Qigong and Tuina Department, Xiyuan Hospital Beijing, China.

"This DVD – the third by the impressively qualified Sydney-based Simon Blow – serves two purposes. Firstly, it is so attractively produced that the curious would surely be induced to investigate further. Secondly, for those already practising, it provides a mnemonic device much more useful than a series of still pictures." **Review by Adyar Bookshop, Sydney 2005.**

These are not medical devices and should not be used to replace any existing medical treatment. Always consult with your health provider if uncertain.

To order products or for more information on:

* Regular classes in Sydney for new and continuing students
* Workshops or if you would be interested in helping organise a workshop in your local area
* Residential Qigong and Meditation retreats
* China Qigong Study Tours for students and advanced training
* Talks, corporate classes, training and presentations
* Wholesale enquiries

Please contact:

Simon Blow
PO Box 446
Summer Hill, NSW 2130
Sydney Australia

Ph: +61 (0)2 9559 8153
Email: info@simonblowqigong.com
Web: **www.simonblowqigong.com**

CDs and Book/DVDs can be ordered online and shipped nationally and internationally.

Bibliography

Publications
Liu Qingshan. *Chinese Fitness*. Massachusetts: YMAA Publication Centre, 1997.

Ni Hua-Ching. T*ao: The Subtle Universal Law and the Integral Way of Life* (2nd edn). California: Seven Star Communications Group, Inc., 1995.

Ni Hua-Ching. *Esoteric Tao Teh Ching*. California: Seven Star Communications Group, Inc., 1992.

Yang, Jwing-Ming. *The Root of Chinese Qigong*, Massachusetts: YMAA Publication Centre, 1997.

Websites
About.com/Taoism, by Elizabeth Reninger: **http://taoism.about.com/b/2009/02/01/the-nei-jing-tu.htm**

Universal Healing Tao: **www.universal-tao.com/tao/inner_alchemy.html**

Art Institute of Chicago: **www.artic.edu/taoism/renaissance/k136/energy.php**

The Tao Bums: **www.thetaobums.com/Looking-for-Nei-Jing-Tu-Qing-Period-Illustration-of-Inner-Circulation-t2350.html**

CPSIA information can be obtained
at www.ICGtesting.com
Printed in the USA
LVHW051300120722
723280LV00004BB/110